Discovering

Geometry

An Investigative Approach

Discovering Geometry with
The Geometer's Sketchpad®

DISCOVERING

MATHEMATICS™

Key Curriculum Press

Innovators in Mathematics Education

Teacher's Materials Project Editor: Elizabeth DeCarli

Editor: Kendra Lockman

Project Administrator: Brady Golden

Writers: Masha Albrecht, Dan Bennett, Sarah Block, Larry Copes, Ned Diamond

Copyeditor: Jill Pellarin

Editorial Production Manager: Christine Osborne

Production Editor: Holly Rudelitsch

Production Supervisor: Ann Rothenbuhler

Production Coordinator: Jennifer Young

Text Designer: Garry Harman

Composition, Technical Art, and Prepress: ICC Macmillan Inc.

Cover Designers: Jill Kongabel, Marilyn Perry, Jensen Barnes

Printer: Data Reproductions

Textbook Product Manager: James Ryan

Executive Editor: Casey FitzSimons

Publisher: Steven Rasmussen

Cover Photos: Credits: Background image: Doug Wilson/Westlight/Corbis. Construction site image: Sonda Dawes/The Image Works. All other images: Ken Karp Photography.

Discovering Geometry Sketches CD-ROM

Key Curriculum Press guarantees that the CD-ROM that accompanies this book is free of defects in materials and workmanship. A defective CD-ROM will be replaced free of charge if returned within 90 days of the purchase date.

Key Curriculum Press
1150 65th Street
Emeryville, CA 94608
510-595-7000
editorial@keypress.com
www.keypress.com

Printed in the United States of America
10 9 8 7 6 5 4 3 2   13 12 11 10 09 08   ISBN 978-1-55953-897-8

Contents

Lesson numbers here refer to the corresponding lesson in *Discovering Geometry*. Not every lesson in the student book is represented here. For example, there are no Sketchpad lessons for Chapter 10.

Chapter 4

Chapter 5

Chapter 6

Chapter 7

Introduction

In *Discovering Geometry*, students working in cooperative groups do investigations, often using compass-and-straightedge constructions, to discover properties. Students look for patterns and use inductive reasoning to make conjectures. The Geometer's Sketchpad® brings Dynamic Geometry® construction and exploration tools to state-of-the-art software, enabling students to see changes in geometric figures as they manipulate them. Sketchpad™ includes complete construction, transformation, and coordinate geometry capabilities, as well as the extensibility offered by custom tools, allowing students to discover and explore relationships dynamically and to explore thousands of cases while making and testing their conjectures.

Types of Activities

Most of the activities in this book replace or expand upon selected lessons in *Discovering Geometry: An Investigative Approach*. These activities are designed for one class period and cover the same material as their corresponding lessons in the student book.

In addition, this book includes demonstrations and extensions. Demonstrations are shorter activities that start with a pre-made sketch. Previous experience with Sketchpad is not required, so you may want to use a demonstration in the beginning of the semester to familiarize yourself and your students with the software. You can use these in a variety of ways. One is to present them with a projector and ask the accompanying questions as a basis for class discussion. Another effective method is to ask one or two students to look at a demonstration ahead of time so they can present it to the class. Still another way is to use demonstrations as short activities for students to do. Because demonstrations use pre-made sketches containing action buttons, they require significantly less time than regular activities.

Extensions focus on material that goes beyond that of the student book, and can be used as extra credit assignments or as enrichment activities. The extensions generally assume experience with Sketchpad and require an entire class period.

Using the Activities

To use this book, you may wish to familiarize yourself with the basic capabilities of Sketchpad. You can introduce yourself to these capabilities by doing some of the Guided Tours in *The Geometer's Sketchpad Learning Guide* that comes with the software. We have also included these tours on the CD that comes with this book. Tours 1, 2, and 4 introduce most of the Sketchpad features used in this book. You don't need to have students do the tours, but the skills you acquire by doing them will help you to answer student questions.

The activities in this book don't demand the use of all of Sketchpad's many features. Students should find most, if not all, of the directions they need to use the software in the activities themselves. You can also reproduce the Tool Box and Common Commands page found at the end of this introduction and either give it to students, or post it near your computers for quick reference.

While doing geometric art is a great way to start the school year, we don't recommend you start with the Chapter 0 extensions in this book as students' introduction to Sketchpad. An important reason for starting a geometry course with art is so that students can become familiar with using a compass and a straightedge. Also, the art extensions in Chapter 0 will be easier for students to do after they've gained some Sketchpad experience. You certainly don't need to save the art activities for last. Let your students try them whenever you think it's appropriate.

Each activity in this book has Teacher's Notes, found at the back of the book. The Teacher's Notes include a section titled Lesson Guide, where you'll find suggestions for how to use the activity.

As you know, presenting a *Discovering Geometry* lesson involves more than setting students loose on investigations. You typically spend time at the beginning of class introducing the subject and at the end of class bringing closure to it and working examples. That time, especially the end-of-class closure, is more difficult to find in a computer lab, where the activities are likely to take most of the period. Students may get through the activities but may not be prepared for the exercise set without some in-class practice. So be prepared to spend an extra day on a lesson that you do with Sketchpad. Later in the year, as students get more proficient with Sketchpad and more persistent with problem solving, you might need that extra day less often.

When you choose an activity to do with students, try it out yourself first so you can prepare how you want to introduce the activity, decide whether to divide tasks, anticipate questions, and get a sense of how long it might take. Read the Teacher's Notes and be sure that if any sketches or custom tools are required, they'll be available. Decide whether this is an activity you want all your students to do in the computer lab, or a group of students to do as an extension, or to do yourself as a demonstration on an overhead display. See the section "Using Sketchpad in Different Classroom Settings" in this introduction for ideas. There may be other lessons in *Discovering Geometry* that you think would make good Sketchpad activities.

Don't abandon all other teaching methods in favor of using the computer. Students need a variety of learning experiences, such as hands-on manipulatives, compass-and-straightedge constructions, drawing, paper-and-pencil work, and discussion. Students also need to apply geometry to real-life situations and see where it is used in art and architecture and where it can be found in nature. While Sketchpad can serve as a medium for many of these experiences, its potential will be reached only when students can apply what they learn with it to different situations.

Using the Pre-Made Sketches

One or more sketches accompany every activity in the book. You can find these files on a single CD-ROM that runs both on Macintosh computers and on computers operating with Windows 95 or later. You can open these sketches directly from the CD, or you can copy them onto one or more hard drives. The sketches are also available for download after you register for

Key Online at www.keypress.com/keyonline. Teachers who purchase this book are free to make as many copies of the sketches as needed for their students. The sketches require The Geometer's Sketchpad Version 4 application to open. The CD does not contain the application itself. Read the Getting Started file on the CD for more details.

The sketches fall into three general categories.

Example Sketches: In most of the regular activities and extensions, students do their own constructions, making their own sketches. No pre-made sketch is needed for these activities. However, example sketches are provided for these activities so that you can quickly see a finished construction like the one students are asked to make. On occasion, you may wish to use the pre-made sketches to speed up an investigation, especially with students who are just learning how to use the software.

Required Sketches: In demonstrations and some activities, students start with a pre-made sketch (as named in the activity and in the Teacher's Notes). These sketches enable students to move straight to investigating relationships in complicated constructions.

Regular Polygon Custom Tools: Constructions of regular polygons, particularly squares, come up in several activities. It's handy to use custom tools for these. You may choose to have students make their own custom tools at least for a square and an equilateral triangle. Or you can have them use the tools in the sketch **Polygons.gsp,** included on the CD in the **Custom Tools** folder and with the application itself. (To use the tools in **Polygons.gsp** on a particular occasion, open the sketch, then access its tools from the Custom Tools menu of any other open sketch. To make these tools permanently available, move the file **Polygons.gsp** into the Tool Folder, which is located alongside the application itself on your hard disk.)

Using Sketchpad in Different Classroom Settings

Different schools have different settings in which students use computers. Sketchpad was designed with this in mind, and you can optimize its display features for these various settings. You also need to adapt your teaching strategies to available resources. Here are some suggestions for teaching with and using Sketchpad in a classroom with one computer, one computer and a computer projection device, several computers, or in a computer lab.

A CLASSROOM WITH ONE COMPUTER

Perhaps the best use of a single computer is to have small groups of students take turns using it. Each group can investigate or confirm conjectures they have made while working at their desks or tables using traditional tools such as paper and pencil or compass and straightedge. In that case, each group would have an opportunity during a class period to use the computer for a short time. Alternatively, you can give each group a day on which to do an investigation on the computer while other groups are doing the same or different investigations at their desks. A single computer without a computer projector or large-screen monitor has limited use as a demonstration tool.

A CLASSROOM WITH ONE COMPUTER AND A COMPUTER PROJECTOR

Having a computer projector considerably increases your teaching options. You or a student can act as a sort of emcee to an investigation, asking the class questions such as: "What should we try next?" "Which objects should I reflect?" "What do you notice as I move this point?" Sketchpad becomes a "dynamic chalkboard" on which you or your students can draw precise, complex figures that can be distorted and transformed in an infinite variety of ways. Watching someone use Sketchpad as a demonstration tool is a good way for students to learn some fundamentals of the program before they go to the computer lab. You can also model good Sketchpad presentation techniques for students. Use large and bold text styles and thick lines to make text and figures clearly visible from all corners of a classroom.

A CLASSROOM WITH SEVERAL COMPUTERS

If you can divide your class into groups of three or four students and give each group access to a computer, you can plan whole lessons around computer investigations. Here are some suggestions for organizing a class in this situation.

- Tell the whole class what they're expected to do.
- Provide students with a written explanation of the investigation or problem they're to work on. In most cases, this will probably be the activity worksheet itself. For some open-ended explorations, you can simply write the problem or question on the chalkboard or type it into the sketch itself. Likewise, students' "written" work can be in the form of sketches with captions and comments.
- Make sure students understand that everybody in a group needs the chance to actually operate the computer.
- Make sure that the students in a group who are not actually operating the computer contribute to the group discussion and give input to the student operating the computer.
- Move among groups, posing questions, giving help if needed, and keeping students on task.
- Summarize students' findings in a whole-class discussion to bring closure to the lesson.

A CLASSROOM OR LAB WITH A COMPUTER FOR EVERY STUDENT

Teachers using Sketchpad often find that even if enough computers are available for students to work individually, it's still best to have students work in pairs. Students learn best when they communicate about what they're learning, and students working together can better stimulate ideas and help one another. If you do have students working at their own computers, encourage them to talk about what they're doing and to compare their findings with those of their neighbors— they *should* peek over one another's shoulders. The suggestions above for students working in small groups apply to students working in pairs as well.

Evaluating work students do on computers presents special challenges. Here are a few suggestions for different methods you can use. You'll probably want to combine several methods in your evaluation.

Method	Advantages	Disadvantages
Viewing student work on their monitors (and possibly signing off on it as you go around the room)	• Very simple, and you'll be doing it anyway	• Minimal written record • Often you don't get to every student during the class period
Collecting completed photocopies of activity sheets	• Easy to collect and assess • Worksheets are well structured to provide guidance to students	• Result has no dynamic information • Result has no constructions • Worksheets can lack flexibility and don't allow as much exploration
Collecting printouts of student sketches	• Easy to collect and assess	• Depends on your printer availability (having the whole class trying to print at the end of the period is not practical) • Printout is not dynamic, so you can't tell whether the constructions are really correct
Collecting work in student file folders on a network	• The work you assess is dynamic • Easy to collect	• Requires a network • Can be time-consuming to assess multiple sketches
Collecting student work on one or more portable storage devices	• The work is dynamic • Doesn't require access to a network	• Collection process can be complicated • Can be time-consuming to assess multiple sketches

Tool Box and Common Commands

Tool Box

Selection Arrow tool: Click objects in sketch to select them. Drag objects to move them. To deselect everything, click in a blank space in the sketch.

Point tool: Click in blank space in the sketch area to construct an independent point, or click on an object to construct a point on that object.

Compass (Circle) tool: Click to construct the center point, drag to construct the circle, and release to construct the radius control point. The center and radius control points can be independent points or points on objects.

Straightedge (Segment) tool: Click to construct the first point, drag to construct the straight object, and release to create second point. (Press and the hold icon to pull out the **Segment, Ray,** and **Line** tools.)

Text tool: Double-click in blank space to create a caption. Click an object to display or hide its label. Drag a label to reposition it. Double-click a label to change it.

Custom tools: Press and hold the icon to display commands for creating and using custom tools.

General

To undo your most recent action: Choose **Undo** from the Edit menu.

To hide an object: Select the object and choose **Hide** from the Display menu.

To show, hide, or change a label: Use the **Text** tool.

The Escape Key: Press the Esc key multiple times to stop caption editing, choose the **Arrow** tool, deselect all objects, stop all animation, and erase all visible traces.

Keyboard Shortcuts for many commands are listed alongside the commands in the menus.

Construct Menu

Parallel or **Perpendicular Line:** Select a point and a segment, line, or ray.

Midpoint: Select a segment.

Angle Bisector: Select three points on the angle, making sure that the vertex is the second point you select.

Arc on Circle: Select a circle and two points on the circle. The arc will be constructed counterclockwise from the first point to the second.

Transform Menu

To translate objects by a marked vector: To designate the translation vector, select the starting point and the ending point of the vector and choose **Mark Vector.** Select the objects you want to translate and choose **Translate.**

To reflect objects: To designate the line of reflection, select a segment, ray, or line and choose **Mark Mirror.** Select the objects you want to reflect and choose **Reflect.**

To rotate objects by a marked angle: To designate the angle, select a point on the initial side of the angle, the vertex, and a point on the final side of the angle. Then choose **Mark Angle.** To designate the center of rotation, select a point and choose **Mark Center.** Select the objects you want to rotate and choose **Rotate.**

Measure Menu

Length: Select one or more segments.

Distance: Select two points, or a point and a line.

Angle: Select three points: a point on the initial side, the vertex, and a point on the final side.

To use the calculator: Choose **Calculate.** To enter a measurement into a calculation, click on the measurement itself in the sketch.

Lesson 0.2 • Line Designs

Extension

You can use straight lines to create designs that appear to curve. On page 8 of your book is a line design called the *astrid*. In this extension, you'll learn how to use Sketchpad to create a dynamic version of the astrid.

Investigation: The Astrid

Sketch

In Steps 1–10, you'll construct two segments with a common endpoint and equally spaced points along them.

Step 1   In a new sketch, construct point *A* and another point, *B*, just to the right of it.

Step 2   Select, in order, point *A* and point *B* and choose **Transform | Mark Vector.**

Step 3   Select point *B* and choose **Transform | Translate.** Translate by the marked vector to construct point *B′*.

Step 4   Translate point *B′* by the same marked vector to construct point *B″*. Keep translating the most recently constructed point until you have about ten points in a line.

Step 5   Drag point *A* and point *B* to see how they affect the other points.

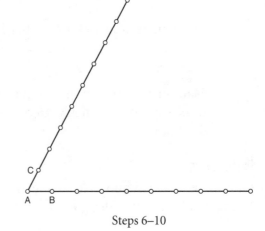

Steps 1–5

Step 6   Construct point *C* above point *A*. (Point *C* should be about as far from point *A* as point *B*.)

Step 7   Select, in order, point *A* and point *C* and choose **Transform | Mark Vector.**

Step 8   Translate point *C* by this marked vector and repeat to construct the same number of points as you constructed in the direction of vector *AB* (about ten).

Step 9   Drag point *C* to see how it affects the other points.

Steps 6–10

Step 10   Draw a segment from point *A* to the last point at the end of each row of points.

Step 11   Draw segments to connect the points, as shown on the next page.

Step 12   Hide all the points except points *A, B,* and *C,* and add color to the lines in your design by using the **Color** palette in the Display menu.

Step 13   Double-click on the segment that passes through points *A* and *C* to mark it as a reflection mirror.

(continued)

Step 14 Select all the segments and choose **Transform | Reflect.**

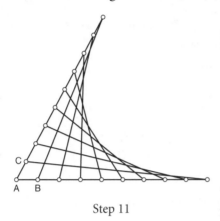

Step 11

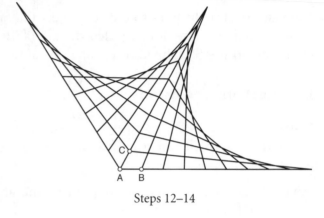

Steps 12–14

Step 15 Double-click on the segment that passes through points *A* and *B* to mark it as a mirror; then reflect all the segments again to make a design like the one shown here.

Investigate

1. This design has just one line of symmetry. Where is it?

2. Drag points *A*, *B*, and *C* to see how they change your design.

    a. Manipulate your design so that it has exactly two lines of symmetry. Describe the lines.

    b. Manipulate your design so that it has four lines of symmetry. Describe the lines.

    c. Manipulate your design so that it has three lines of symmetry. Describe the lines.

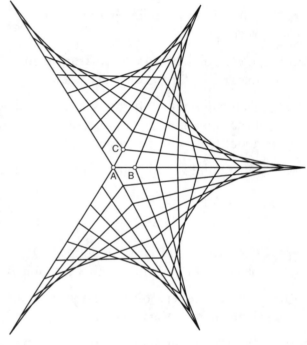

Step 15

EXPLORE MORE

Open a new sketch and experiment with this method or other methods to make different line designs.

Lesson 0.3 • Circle Designs

Extension

A daisy design is a simple design that you can create using only a compass. From the basic daisy, you can create more complex designs based on the regular hexagon.

Investigation: Hexagons and Daisies

Sketch

Step 1 In a new sketch, construct circle *AB* (a circle with center *A* and radius control point *B*).

Step 2 Construct circle *BA*. Be sure you start your circle with the cursor positioned at point *B* and that you don't let go of the mouse until the cursor is positioned at point *A*.

Step 3 Construct the two points of intersection of these circles.

Step 4 Using the intersection points as centers, continue constructing circles to existing points. All these circles should have equal radii. When you're done, your sketch should look like this figure.

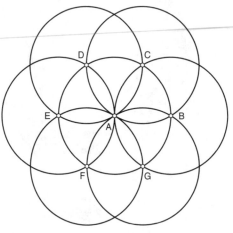

Steps 1–4

Step 5 If your last circle refuses to be constructed, you're probably releasing the mouse on the intersection of three circles. In this case, select two circles and construct their intersection with the Construct menu. Then use this point to construct your final circle.

Step 6 Use the **Segment** tool to add some lines to your design; then drag point *B* and observe how your design changes.

Investigate

1. Make a design using the circles in your sketch. There are many possibilities. You can construct polygon interiors and experiment with shading and color. You also can construct arcs (select a circle and two points on it) and arc sectors and arc segment interiors (select an arc). However, you can probably get better results by printing the basic design and adding color and shading by hand.

(continued)

2. The six points of your daisy define six vertices of a regular hexagon. Use these points as the basis for hexagon or star designs like these. Once you have all the lines and polygon interiors you want, you can hide unneeded points. Don't hide your original two points, though, as you can use these points to manipulate your figure.

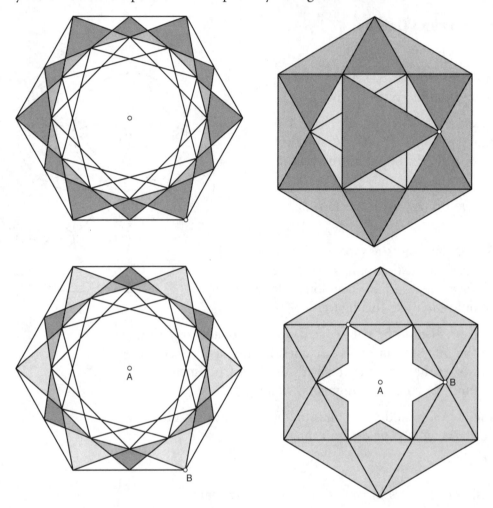

Lesson 0.3 • Rosettes

In Lesson 0.3, you used a compass to make daisies and other circle designs.
You can also use The Geometer's Sketchpad to make designs based on the
daisy, such as the rosette. Rosettes appear as a design element in many
cultures. For example, rosettes appear in Roman mosaics from the first
century B.C.E. Here is how to make a rosette.

Sketch

Step 1 In a new sketch, use the **Compass** tool to construct a
daisy. Make complete circles. Do not stop at the perimeter
of the circle. Use the **Text** tool to label the control point
of the original circle. This will allow you to easily resize
your design if you need to.

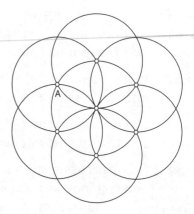

Step 2 Find a point midway between two points on the inner
circle. Use it to construct six more circles with the same
radius as the others, with centers on the original circle.
You now have a 12-petal daisy and 12 equally spaced
circles around the original circle.

Step 3 Repeat Step 2 until you have a 24-petal daisy and 24 equally
spaced circles around the original circle.

Step 4 Construct a set of circles concentric to the original circle and
going through each of the points of intersection of the 24-petal
daisy.

Investigate

Decorate your rosette design, adding or deleting circles as you choose. If
you want to print your design and decorate it by hand, be sure to first
choose **File | Print Preview** and select Scale To Fit Page.

Lesson 0.4 • Op Art

A tumbling block design is commonly found in Amish quilt patterns. It's an example of op art because of the interesting optical effect suggested by its name. You can create a tumbling block design very efficiently with Sketchpad using translations.

Investigation: Tumbling Blocks

Sketch

Step 1 In a new sketch, construct a regular hexagon. Use your own method or a **Custom** tool such as **6/Hexagon (Inscribed).**

Step 2 If you used a tool that constructs the hexagon's interior, click on the interior to select it; then delete it.

Step 3 Construct the center of the hexagon (if it doesn't already exist) by constructing the intersection of any two diagonals.

Step 4 Construct segments and two polygon interiors to make your hexagon look like this figure. To construct a polygon interior, select the vertices of the polygon; then choose **Construct | Polygon Interior.**

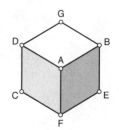

Steps 1–4

In Steps 5–7, you'll translate this figure to create a row of blocks.

Step 5 Select points *D* and *B,* in that order, and choose **Transform | Mark Vector.**

Step 6 Choose **Edit | Select All,** then click on each of the points to deselect them. Translate by vector *DB.*

Step 7 Translate the new block two more times so that you have a row of four blocks. Drag a control point of your original hexagon if you need to scale your blocks.

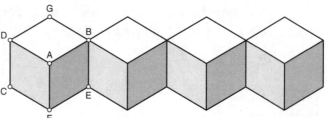

Steps 5–7

Step 8 Mark *DF* as vector.

Step 9 Choose **Edit | Select All** (including the points) and translate the row of blocks by vector *DF.*

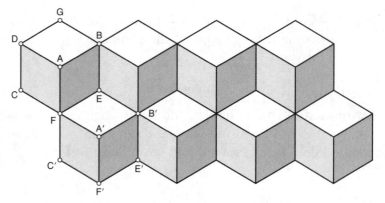

Steps 8 and 9

(continued)

Step 10 Mark *GC′* as vector.

Step 11 Choose **Edit | Select All** and translate the two rows of blocks by vector *GC′* to create four rows in all.

Step 12 To make your design neater, hide all points except those that control your original block, *A* and *B*.

Step 13 Drag point *B* and observe how you can change your design.

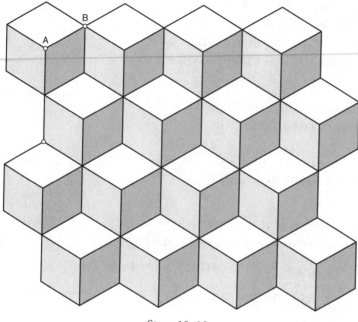

Steps 10–12

Investigate

1. Describe the shapes that make up your design.

2. Describe the optical effect of this design.

EXPLORE MORE

1. Animate point *B* by selecting it and choosing **Display | Animate Point.** You can control the speed from the Motion Controller or by setting up a button (choose **Edit | Action Buttons | Animation**).

2. Use Sketchpad to make another op art design of your own.

.son 0.6 • Islamic Tile Designs

In this activity you'll construct a square-based knot design similar to designs created by Islamic artists.

Investigation: Knotted Squares

Sketch

Step 1　In a new sketch, construct a square and its center using a **Custom** tool such as **4/Square (Inscribed).** If your tool constructs the square's interior, click on the interior and delete it. If your tool doesn't construct the square's center, construct it and hide any auxiliary lines.

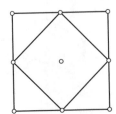

Step 2　Construct the midpoints of the sides of the square and connect them to construct a smaller square within the square.

Steps 1 and 2

Step 3　Double-click the center to mark it as a center for rotation.

Step 4　Select the entire figure and choose **Transform | Rotate.** Rotate the figure by 45°.

Step 5　Construct eight points of intersection where the small squares intersect and eight more points where the large squares intersect.

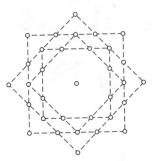

Step 6　Select the entire figure and choose **Display | Line Width | Dashed.**

Now you have the basic outline of the design, and you're ready to draw over it to make it appear knotted.

Step 7　Study your design and plan out how to draw solid segments over some of the dashed ones to make the design appear as two knotted squares. Try it on your own, or follow the next step to see one way to do it. After you've drawn the first of these segments, choose **Display | Line Width | Thick** to change this and all subsequent segments.

Step 8　Starting from the topmost corner and going counterclockwise, draw segments to show the top corner going over the other square, then under, over, under, over, and so on.

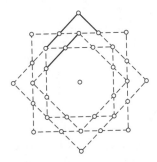 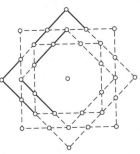 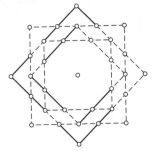

Step 8

(continued)

Discovering Geometry with The Geometer's Sketchpad
©2008 Key Curriculum Press

Lesson 0.6 • Islamic Tile Designs (continued)

Step 9 Now do the same thing for the other square. If you want, you can choose a different line width for the second square.

Step 10 Put the finishing touches on the design: Select each of the dashed segments where they remain visible and choose **Display | Hide Segments.** Construct polygon interiors to add color or shading to the design.

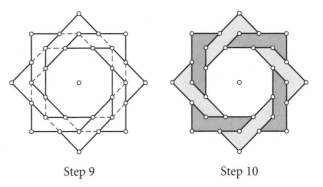

Step 9   Step 10

Now that you have the basic design, you're ready to make a repeating pattern.

Step 11 Select, in order, *A* and *B*. Choose **Transform | Mark Vector.**

Step 12 Select the entire figure; then choose **Transform | Translate** to translate your design by the marked vector. Repeat the translation so that you have a row of knotted squares.

Step 13 Mark vector *CD*, select all, and translate the row of squares twice so that you have three rows.

Step 14 Construct other polygon interiors as you wish. Drag the center point of the top left design unit to manipulate the design until it's aligned and sized the way you like it. Hide any points you don't need.

EXPLORE MORE

Experiment with creating Islamic-style designs of your own.

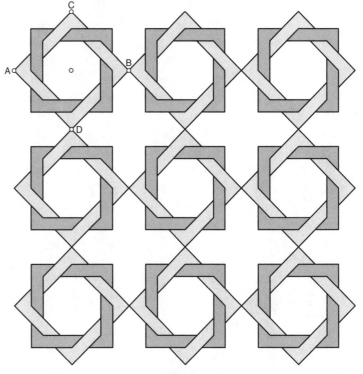

Steps 11–13

Using Your Algebra Skills 1 • Midpoint

In this activity you will discover a method for finding the midpoint of a line segment using the coordinate grid.

Investigation: The Coordinate Midpoint Property

Sketch

Step 1   Open a new sketch and choose **Graph | Show Grid.** Also be sure **Snap Points** is checked in the Graph menu.

Step 2   Construct segment *AB* anywhere on your grid.

Step 3   Select $\overline{AB}$ and choose **Construct | Midpoint.** Change the label of this point to *Midpoint*.

Step 4   Select all three points on $\overline{AB}$ and choose **Measure | Coordinates.**

Step 5   Line up the three measurements vertically so it is easier for you to compare the numbers.

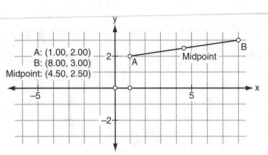

Investigate

1. To look for patterns, drag the endpoints of your segment and watch the six coordinate measurements carefully. It might be easier to focus on the *x*-coordinates first, then pay attention to the *y*-coordinates later. The pattern is also easier to see when the segment is shorter and in the first quadrant. Keep experimenting until you are sure you have found a pattern that describes the relationship between the coordinates of the endpoints of a segment and the coordinates of the segment's midpoint. Record your observations.

2. Now you can generalize by writing a conjecture using variables. Suppose that one endpoint of a segment has coordinates (x_1, y_1) and the other has the coordinates (x_2, y_2). Record the coordinates of the midpoint and write your results as a conjecture (Coordinate Midpoint Property).

3. In the Graph menu, turn off **Snap Points.** Now drag your segment into a new position. Test your conjecture using the coordinates of the new endpoints. Record your results.

EXPLORE MORE

Construct a segment and measure the coordinates of its endpoints: Choose **Abscissa(x)** and **Ordinate(y)** from the Measure menu to find the two coordinates of each endpoint. Then use the calculator to calculate each coordinate of the midpoint. (You may need to use parentheses in the calculator.) Select, in order, the *x*-coordinate and the *y*-coordinate of the midpoint and choose **Graph | Plot As (x, y).** Drag an endpoint and report on your results. Did you successfully calculate the midpoint's coordinates?

Lesson 1.5 • Triangles

In this activity you'll experiment with both ordinary triangles and triangles that were constructed with constraints. The constraints limit what you can change in the triangle when you drag so that certain relationships among angles and sides always hold. By observing these relationships, you will classify the triangles.

Investigation: Classifying Triangles

Sketch

Step 1 Open the sketch **Triangles.gsp.**

Step 2 Drag different vertices of each of the four triangles to observe and compare how the triangles are constrained.

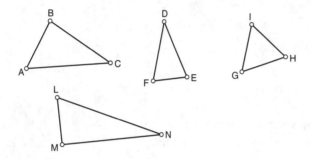

Investigate

1. Which of the triangles seems the least constrained (the easiest to change by dragging)? Explain.

2. Which of the triangles seems the most constrained (the hardest to change by dragging)? Explain.

3. Recall the definitions of *acute, obtuse,* and *right* angles. These terms are also used to classify triangles. Measure the three angles in △*ABC.* (To measure an angle, select only three points on the angle, with the vertex as the second selection, and choose **Measure | Angle.**) Determine whether each angle is acute or obtuse. Now drag a vertex of your triangle. How many acute angles can a triangle have?

4. How many obtuse angles can a triangle have?

5. Triangle *ABC* can be either an obtuse triangle or an acute triangle. One other triangle in the sketch can also be either acute or obtuse. Which triangle is it?

6. Which triangle is always a right triangle, no matter what you drag?

7. Which triangle is always an equiangular triangle, no matter what you drag?

(continued)

Discovering Geometry with The Geometer's Sketchpad
©2008 Key Curriculum Press

8. *Scalene, isosceles,* and *equilateral* are terms used to classify triangles by relationships among their sides. Measure the lengths of the three sides of △*ABC*. If none of the side lengths are equal, the triangle is a scalene triangle. If two or more of the sides are equal in length, the triangle is isosceles. If all three sides are equal in length, it is equilateral. Because △*ABC* has no constraints, it can be any type of triangle. But which type of triangle is △*ABC* most of the time?

9. Name a triangle other than △*ABC* that is scalene most of the time.

10. Which triangle (or triangles) is (are) always isosceles, no matter what you drag?

11. Which triangle is always equilateral, no matter what you drag?

In Questions 12–16, tell whether the triangle described is possible or not possible. To check your answer, try manipulating the triangles in the sketch to make one that fits the description. If the triangle is possible, sketch an example on your paper.

12. Obtuse isosceles triangle

13. Acute right triangle

14. Obtuse equiangular triangle

15. Isosceles right triangle

16. Acute scalene triangle

17. Write definitions for *acute triangle, obtuse triangle, right triangle, scalene triangle, isosceles triangle,* and *equilateral triangle.*

EXPLORE MORE

1. Construct a triangle that stays a right triangle no matter what you drag, like △*LMN*. For ideas, choose **Display │ Show All Hidden** in the sketch **Triangles.gsp.** Use the Help menu if you need to.

2. In a new sketch, construct an isosceles triangle that always stays isosceles or an equilateral triangle that is always equilateral.

Lesson 1.6 • Classifying Parallelograms

Demonstration

In this demonstration you'll manipulate four specially constructed quadrilaterals: a parallelogram, a rhombus, a rectangle, and a square. You'll see how they behave and how they are related to one another.

Sketch

Step 1   Open the sketch **Parallelogram Demo.gsp.**

Step 2   Choose the **Arrow** tool and drag different vertices of each shape. Play for a minute to get a feel for how each point controls the shape.

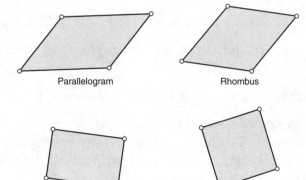

Parallelogram   Rhombus

Rectangle   Square

Investigate

1. Which of the four shapes is the most flexible? Explain.

2. Which of the four shapes is the least flexible? Explain.

3. Write a sentence or two about the flexibility of the other two shapes. Is one more flexible than the other? Explain.

4. All four shapes are parallelograms, but the rectangle, rhombus, and square have additional properties. What properties do all four parallelograms have in common?

Sketch

Step 3   While watching the four shapes, press the *Make Equilateral* button. You should see one or more of the shapes change. If you don't, try dragging different points to change each shape, then press *Make Equilateral* again. Once each shape is equilateral, don't change it until you've answered the following questions.

Investigate

5. Which shapes changed when you pressed *Make Equilateral*?

6. Which shapes didn't change when you pressed *Make Equilateral*? Explain.

7. What shape does the parallelogram look like when it's equilateral?

8. What shape does the rectangle look like when it's equilateral?

(continued)

Discovering Geometry with The Geometer's Sketchpad

Sketch

Step 4 Drag different points to change each shape.

Step 5 While watching the four shapes, press *Make Equiangular*. Once each shape is equiangular, don't change it until you've answered the following questions.

Investigate

9. Which shapes changed when you pressed *Make Equiangular*?

10. Which shapes didn't change when you pressed *Make Equiangular*? Explain.

11. What shape does the parallelogram look like when it's equiangular?

12. What shape does the rhombus look like when it's equiangular?

Sketch

Step 6 Drag different points to change each shape.

Step 7 Press both *Make Equiangular* and *Make Equilateral,* in either order.

Investigate

13. What shape do all the parallelograms look like when they are both equiangular and equilateral?

Drag points and press the buttons as needed to answer the following questions.

14. Write a definition for *parallelogram.*

15. Write a definition for *rhombus.*

16. Write a definition for *rectangle.*

17. Write a definition for *square.*

18. Is a rectangle always, sometimes, or never a rhombus? Explain.

19. Is a square always, sometimes, or never a rectangle? Explain.

20. Is a parallelogram always, sometimes, or never a square? Explain.

21. This is a concept map showing the relationships among the different types of parallelograms. This type of concept map is known as a **Venn diagram**. Fill in the missing names.

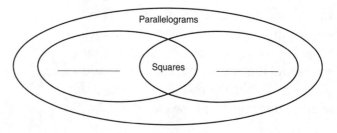

Lesson 1.6 • Special Quadrilaterals

Investigation 1: Trapezoids and Kites

Sketch

Step 1 Open the sketch **Special Quadrilaterals.gsp** to the page Trapezoid & Kite.

Step 2 Drag various parts of each quadrilateral. Each one has a set of constraints in its construction that keeps it what it is.

Step 3 Measure the slopes of the four sides of the trapezoid by selecting the sides and choosing **Measure | Slope.**

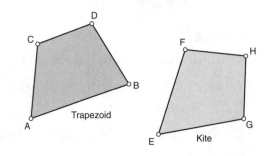

Investigate

1. If lines (or segments) have the same slope, they are **parallel.** How many pairs of sides in the trapezoid are parallel?

2. If you're very careful, it's possible to drag vertices so that both pairs of opposite sides in the trapezoid are parallel, or at least close to it. However, in that case, the figure is no longer a trapezoid. Given that restriction, define *trapezoid*.

3. Measure the lengths of the four sides of the kite. Which sides are equal in length?

4. If you're very careful, it's possible to drag vertices so that all four sides in the kite are equal in length, or at least close to it. In that case, the figure is no longer a kite. Given that restriction, define *kite*.

Investigation 2: Parallelograms

Sketch

Step 1 Go to the page Special Quads.

Step 2 Drag various parts of these quadrilaterals.

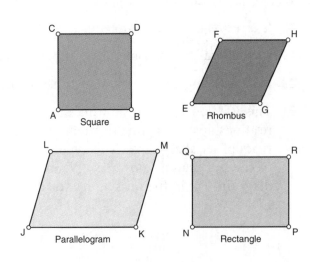

Investigate

Each quadrilateral has a different set of constraints in its construction that keeps it what it is. For example, no matter what part you drag, the square stays a square. You can drag vertices of the rhombus to make different shapes, but you'll still have a rhombus.

1. Measure the slopes of the sides of the parallelogram. Drag parts of the figure. How many pairs of sides are parallel? Define *parallelogram*.

(continued)

Discovering Geometry with The Geometer's Sketchpad

2. Measure the angles in the rectangle. (To measure an angle, select three points on the angle, with the vertex as your second selection, and choose **Measure | Angle.**) Drag parts of the figure. Define *rectangle*.

3. Measure the side lengths in the rhombus. Drag parts of the figure. Define *rhombus*.

4. Measure the side lengths and angles of the square. Define *square*.

5. Drag the rhombus so that it's also a rectangle (or at least close to it). What's the best name for this shape?

6. Drag the rectangle so that it's also a rhombus (or at least close to it). What's the best name for this shape?

7. Based on your observations in Questions 5 and 6, write a definition of *square* different from your answer to Question 4.

In Questions 8–12, complete the sentence with *always, sometimes,* or *never.*

8. A parallelogram is _____ a square.

9. A rectangle is _____ a rhombus.

10. A square is _____ a rhombus.

11. A rectangle is _____ a parallelogram.

12. A parallelogram that is not a rectangle is _____ a square.

EXPLORE MORE

1. See if you can come up with methods for constructing trapezoids and kites that always stay trapezoids and kites. Describe your methods.

2. Open a new sketch and see if you can come up with ways to construct special parallelograms. Describe your methods.

Lesson 1.7 • Defining Circle Terms

A **circle** is the set of all points in a plane at a given distance from a given point in the plane. The given distance is called the **radius** of the circle, and the given point is called its **center.** The term *radius* also refers to a certain type of segment in a circle, which you will define. In this demonstration you will also define and observe properties of other objects related to circles.

Lines and Segments

Sketch

Step 1 Open the sketch **Circle Terms Demo.gsp** to the page Lines and Segments.

Step 2 Press *Show Radius,* and drag the red point to explore the segment's properties. Press the button again to hide the radius.

Step 3 Repeat Step 2 for each of the other terms.

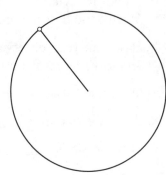

Investigate

1. Write good definitions for *radius, chord, diameter, tangent,* and *secant.*

2. How are diameters and chords related? Draw a diagram or write a sentence to show the relationship.

3. Can two circles be tangent to the same line at the same point? Draw a sketch and explain.

Congruent and Concentric Circles

Sketch

Step 4 Go to the page Congruent and Concentric in the same sketch.

Step 5 Drag the four points and observe the changes.

Investigate

4. A circle is usually named after its center point. Note that two of the circles in the sketch are named by two points, the center point and the radius control point. Explain why this method of naming might be clearer.

5. Define *concentric circles* and *congruent circles* based on the information in the sketch.

(continued)

Discovering Geometry with The Geometer's Sketchpad

Lesson 1.7 • Defining Circle Terms (continued)

Major and Minor Arcs

Sketch

Step 6 Go to the page Major and Minor Arcs in the same sketch.

Step 7 Drag points *B, C, D,* and *E* and observe the changes.

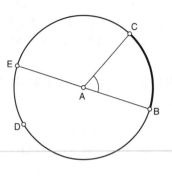

Investigate

6. What type of chord is $\overline{EB}$? Explain.

7. Write definitions for *semicircle, minor arc,* and *major arc* based on the information in the sketch. Why are the semicircle and major arc named with three letters?

8. Write a definition for *central angle.* How is the measure of the central angle related to the measures of the minor and major arcs whose endpoints it passes through? Drag points in the sketch to verify this.

Lesson 1.7 • Circles

A **circle** is the set of all points in a plane at a given distance from a given point in the plane. In this activity, you'll construct circles and various lines, angles, and segments associated with circles.

Investigation: Defining Circle Terms

Sketch

Step 1 Use the **Circle** tool to construct a circle. Two points, *A* and *B*, define your circle. Drag each point to see how it affects the circle.

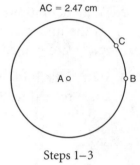

AC = 2.47 cm

A circle is usually named after its center point. This circle would be called circle *A*. It's often convenient to name a Sketchpad circle after both points that define it, so you could also call this circle *AB*.

Step 2 Construct point *C* on the circle.

Step 3 Select points *A* and *C* and choose **Measure | Distance.**

Steps 1–3

Investigate

1. Drag point *C* around the circle. What do you notice about the distance *AC*? How does this observation relate to the definition of a circle?

2. Construct segment *AB*. This segment is called a **radius**. Its length is also called the radius. You can change the radius of this circle by dragging point *A* or point *B*. One way to measure a circle's radius is to select the circle itself and then choose **Measure | Radius.** Find and describe two other ways you can measure the radius of a circle using different commands from the Measure menu.

3. Construct a circle centered at point *A* with control point *D* as shown. Drag point *D* so that circle *AD* goes inside and outside circle *AB*. If two or more coplanar circles share the same center, they are **concentric** circles. How many circles can share the same center? (Can you see why it might be convenient to name circles after two points?)

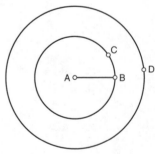

4. Construct a point *E* anywhere in your sketch. Select segment *AB* and point *E* and choose **Construct | Circle By Center + Radius.** Drag point *B* to see how it affects your new circle. Circle *E* and circle *AB* are **congruent** circles. Write a definition of *congruent circles*.

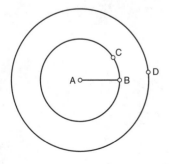

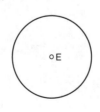

(continued)

Discovering Geometry with The Geometer's Sketchpad
©2008 Key Curriculum Press

Lesson 1.7 • Circles (continued)

An **arc of a circle** is two points on the circle and a continuous part of the circle between them. The two points are called **endpoints.**

Sketch

Step 4   Select, in order, circle *AB*, point *B*, and point *C*. Choose **Construct | Arc On Circle.** While this arc is selected, choose **Display | Line Width** and check **Thick.**

Step 5   Select, in order, circle *AB*, point *C*, and point *B*, and choose **Construct | Arc On Circle.** This should give you a different arc from the one you constructed in Step 4. Change the color or thickness of this arc.

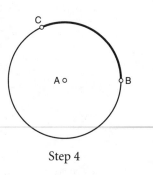

Step 4

Step 6   Construct segments from *C* to *A* and from *B* to *A*. ∠*CAB* is called a **central angle.** Measure ∠*CAB* by selecting in order, points *C*, *A*, and *B*, and then choosing **Measure | Angle.** Then measure the two arcs you just created. Click on the arc to select it, then choose **Measure | Arc Angle.** Arrange the measures on the screen. Note that Sketchpad does not use three letters to name the major arc.

Investigate

Two points on a circle divide the circle into two arcs. Here, one arc from point *B* to point *C* is less than half the circle. This is called a **minor arc.** The other arc, which is more than half the circle, is called a **major arc.** The minor arc is named after its two endpoints: $\overarc{BC}$ or $\overarc{CB}$. You use three points to name a major arc. The first and last letters come from the endpoints, and the middle letter is any other point on the arc.

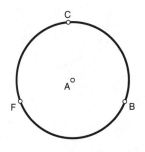

5. Construct a point *F* on the major arc. (To do this, select the arc and choose **Construct | Point On Arc.**) Write two names for the major arc.

6. Drag point *C* until it appears that points *B* and *C* divide the circle into congruent halves. An arc that is half a circle is called a **semicircle.** Do you think semicircles should be named by two points or by three? Explain. Name the semicircles in your sketch. Add a point to the sketch, if necessary.

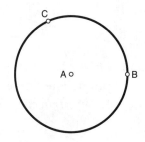

7. Now look at the measures of the central angle and the arcs. How is the measure of the central angle related to the measure of the minor arc whose endpoints it passes through? The major arc with the same endpoints?

Next, you'll look at segments and lines through circles. Delete or hide segments *AC* and *AB*.

8. Construct segment *BC*. Drag point *C* and observe its behavior. Segment *BC* is a **chord** of the circle. Define *chord.*

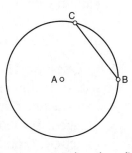

(continued)

9. Drag point *C* so that $\overline{BC}$ passes through point *A*. In that position, $\overline{BC}$ is a special chord called a **diameter** of the circle. Define *diameter*. (*Note:* Like the term *radius, diameter* can refer to a segment as well as to the length of the segment.)

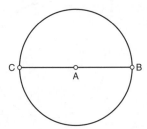

10. Construct a line through points *B* and *C*. (The line will overlap $\overline{BC}$.) Drag point *C* again. Line *BC* is a **secant** of the circle. Define *secant*.

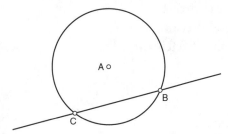

11. Drag point *C* toward point *B* until the two points coincide in a single point. The line is no longer a secant. Instead, it is called a **tangent.** Define *tangent*.

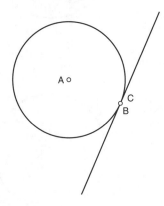

EXPLORE MORE

1. In Question 9, you dragged an endpoint of a chord so that it temporarily became a diameter. But you never actually constructed a diameter that would stay a diameter no matter what you dragged. Try it. Construct a circle and a diameter that stays a diameter.

2. In Question 11, you dragged a point so that a secant was no longer a secant, temporarily becoming a tangent instead. But you never actually constructed a line that would stay a tangent no matter what you dragged. Try it. Construct a circle and a line that is always tangent to the circle. (*Hint:* Imagine how a radius might be related to the tangent line that passes through the endpoint of the radius.)

   Discovering Geometry with The Geometer's Sketchpad
©2008 Key Curriculum Press

Lesson 2.4 • Overlapping Segments

Demonstration

In this demonstration you'll use inductive reasoning to form a conjecture about overlapping segments.

Sketch

Step 1   Open the sketch **Overlapping Segments Demo.gsp.**

Step 2   The sketch is constructed so that $\overline{AB} \cong \overline{CD}$. Drag points and observe the lengths of the segments to verify this is true.

AC = 15.5 cm   BD = 15.5 cm

A ⊢6.3 cm⊣ B ⊣9.2 cm⊢ C ⊢6.3 cm⊣ D

AD = 21.8 cm

Investigate

1. There are six different segments in the sketch. Name them.

2. Which of the segments from Question 1 appear to be congruent to each other (other than $\overline{AB}$ and $\overline{CD}$)? Drag points to help make your conclusions.

3. Segments AC and BD are **overlapping** segments. How do they compare to one another? Summarize your observations in a conjecture (Overlapping Segments Conjecture).

   You used inductive reasoning to write the Overlapping Segments Conjecture. Now you will use deductive reasoning to explain why the conjecture is true.

4. Press *Show Sums*. Complete the following equations:

$$AB + BC = \underline{\qquad} \qquad\qquad BC + CD = \underline{\qquad}$$

5. Use the given sums, and the fact that $\overline{AB} \cong \overline{CD}$, to prove your conjecture from Question 3.

Lesson 2.4 • Overlapping Angles

In this demonstration you'll use inductive reasoning to form a conjecture about overlapping angles.

Sketch

Step 1   Open the sketch **Overlapping Angles Demo.gsp.**

Step 2   The sketch is constructed so that $\angle APC \cong \angle DPB$. Drag points and observe the measures of the angles to verify this is true.

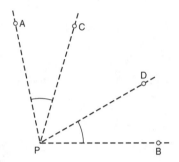

Investigate

1. There are six different angles in the sketch. Name them.

2. Which of the angles from Question 1 appear to be congruent to each other (other than $\angle APC$ and $\angle DPB$)? Drag points to help make your conclusions.

3. Angles *APD* and *CPD* are **overlapping** angles. Press *Show Overlapping angles*. How do $\angle APD$ and $\angle CPD$ compare to one another? Summarize your observations in a conjecture (Overlapping Angles Conjecture).

You used inductive reasoning to write the Overlapping Angles Conjecture. Now you will use deductive reasoning to explain why the conjecture is true.

4. Press *Show Sums*. Complete the following equations:

$$m\angle APC + m\angle CPD = \underline{\quad} \qquad m\angle CPD + m\angle DPB = \underline{\quad}$$

5. Use the given sums, and the fact that $\angle APC \cong \angle DPB$, to prove your conjecture from Question 3.

Discovering Geometry with The Geometer's Sketchpad
©2008 Key Curriculum Press

Lesson 2.5 • Linear Pairs and Vertical Angles   Demonstration

In this demonstration you'll discover two angle relationships.

Linear Pairs

Recall from Lesson 1.3 of your book that two angles form a **linear pair** if they share a vertex and one side, and their non-shared sides lie on a straight line.

Sketch

Step 1   Open the sketch **Intersecting Lines Demo.gsp** to the page Linear Pairs.

Step 2   Drag point *S* around and observe how the angle measures change.

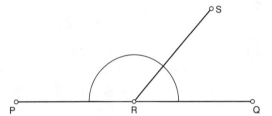

Investigate

1. Are the measures of ∠*PRS* and ∠*SRQ* always equal?

2. Are these measures related in some other way?

3. What do we call two angles if the sum of their measures is 180°?

4. Make a conjecture about linear pairs of angles (Linear Pair Conjecture). Remember to write each conjecture in your notebook, and draw a sketch to go with it.

Vertical Angles

Vertical angles are opposite angles formed by two intersecting lines. Here you'll see how vertical angles are related.

Sketch

Step 3   Go to the page Vertical Angles.

Step 4   Drag any of the points around and watch how the angle measures change.

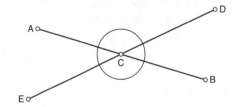

Investigate

5. Which angles always have the same measure?

6. Are any of the angles always supplementary? Which ones?

7. Make a conjecture about vertical angles (Vertical Angles Conjecture). Remember to add the conjecture to your notebook, and draw a sketch to go with it.

8. Use the Linear Pair Conjecture and the diagram to explain why the Vertical Angles Conjecture is true.

Lesson 2.5 • Angle Relationships

When two lines intersect, they form four angles whose vertices are the point of intersection. In this activity you'll investigate relationships between pairs of these angles.

Investigation: Pairs of Angles

Sketch

Step 1   In a new sketch, construct $\overleftrightarrow{AB}$ and $\overleftrightarrow{AC}$. Start the second line at A to make sure it is a control point of both lines.

Step 2   Construct point D on $\overleftrightarrow{AB}$ so that A is between D and B. Also construct E on $\overleftrightarrow{AC}$ so that A is between E and C.

Step 3   Measure the four angles: $\angle BAC$, $\angle CAD$, $\angle DAE$, and $\angle EAB$. (Remember that to measure an angle you need to select three points on the angle, using the vertex as the middle point.)

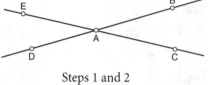

Steps 1 and 2

Investigate

1. Drag points B and C. Record anything you notice about the relationships among the angles.

2. In your sketch, $\angle BAC$ and $\angle CAD$ are a **linear pair** because the outside sides of the angles form a line.

   a. Find all the other linear pairs in your sketch.

   b. Write a conjecture about the relationship between the measures of angles in a linear pair (Linear Pair Conjecture). Choose **Measure | Calculate** and make an appropriate calculation to test your conjecture.

3. When are the angles in a linear pair congruent?

4. In your sketch, $\angle BAC$ and $\angle DAE$ are a pair of **vertical angles.** This name is related to the fact that the angles share the same vertex. $\angle CAD$ and $\angle EAB$ are another pair of vertical angles. Make a conjecture about the measures of vertical angles (Vertical Angles Conjecture).

EXPLORE MORE

1. Two intersecting lines form four angles. If you know the measure of one of the angles, you can find the measures of the other three. Suppose you have three lines intersecting in a single point to form six angles.

   a. How many angle measures do you need to know in order to find the other angle measures?

   b. When are all six angles congruent?

2. Suppose you have four lines intersecting in a single point to form eight angles. Answer Question 1 for this case.

3. Now generalize your results from Questions 1 and 2. Suppose you have n lines intersecting to form $2n$ angles. Answer Question 1 for this case.

Lesson 2.6 • Special Angles on Parallel Lines

In this activity you'll discover relationships among the angles formed when you intersect parallel lines with a third line called a **transversal.**

Investigation 1: Which Angles Are Congruent?

Sketch

Step 1 In a new sketch, construct $\overleftrightarrow{AB}$ and point C, not on $\overleftrightarrow{AB}$.

Step 2 Construct a line parallel to $\overleftrightarrow{AB}$ through point C.

Step 3 Construct $\overleftrightarrow{AC}$. Drag points C and A to make sure you attached the three lines correctly.

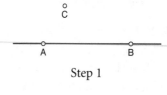
Step 1

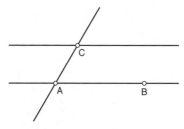

Steps 2 and 3

Step 4 Construct points D, E, F, G, and H as shown.

Step 5 Measure the eight angles in your figure. (Remember that to measure angles you need to select three points on the angle, making sure the middle point is always the vertex.)

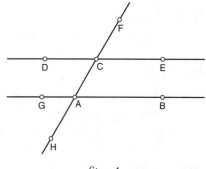
Step 4

Investigate

1. When two parallel lines are cut by a transversal, the pairs of angles formed have specific names and properties. Drag point A or B and determine which angles stay congruent. Also drag the transversal $\overleftrightarrow{AC}$. Describe how many of the eight angles you measured appear to be always congruent.

2. Angles FCE and CAB are a pair of **corresponding angles.**

   a. List all the pairs of corresponding angles in your construction.

   b. Write a conjecture describing what you observe about corresponding angles (CA Conjecture).

3. Angles ECA and CAG are a pair of **alternate interior angles.**

   a. List all the pairs of alternate interior angles in your construction.

   b. Write a conjecture describing what you observe about alternate interior angles (AIA Conjecture).

(continued)

4. Angles *FCE* and *HAG* are a pair of **alternate exterior angles.**

   a. List all the pairs of alternate exterior angles in your construction.

   b. Write a conjecture describing what you observe about alternate exterior angles (AEA Conjecture).

5. Combine the three conjectures you made in Questions 2–4 into a single conjecture about parallel lines that are cut by a transversal (Parallel Lines Conjecture).

6. Suppose, in a similar sketch, all you knew was that the angle pairs described above had the properties you observed. Could you be sure that the original pair of lines were parallel? Try to answer this question first without using the computer.

Investigation 2: Is the Converse True?

Sketch

Step 1 In a new sketch, construct two lines that are not quite parallel. Intersect both lines with a transversal.

Step 2 Measure all eight angles formed by the three lines. Add points if you need them.

Step 3 Move the lines until the pairs of angles match the conjectures you made in the previous investigation.

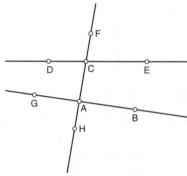

Investigate

1. Lines with equal slopes are parallel. To check if your lines are parallel, measure their slopes. Write a new conjecture summarizing your conclusions (Converse of the Parallel Lines Conjecture).

EXPLORE MORE

1. Angles *ECA* and *BAC* in Step 4 in Investigation 1 are sometimes called **consecutive interior angles.** In a new sketch, find all pairs of consecutive interior angles and make a conjecture describing their relationship.

2. Angles *FCD* and *HAG* in that same figure are sometimes called **consecutive exterior angles.** Find pairs of consecutive exterior angles in the figure and make a conjecture describing their relationship.

3. You can use the Converse of the Parallel Lines Conjecture to construct parallel lines. Construct a pair of intersecting lines $\overleftrightarrow{AB}$ and $\overleftrightarrow{AC}$ as shown. Select, in order, points *C*, *A*, and *B*, and choose **Transform | Mark Angle.** Double-click point *C* to mark it as a center for rotation. You figure out the rest. Explain why this works.

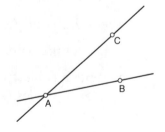

Using Your Algebra Skills 2 • Slope

Here you will discover a method for finding the slope of a line. You may have learned about calculating slope in a previous class.

Investigation 1: The Slope of a Line

If you are a skier, you might describe the slope of a hill you skied down. If you are a carpenter, you might describe the slope of a roof you built. An economist might describe the slope of a graph. In this activity you'll first experiment with the slopes of various lines. Then you will play a game, with a partner, that challenges you to recognize various slopes. Finally, you will make a conjecture about how to calculate the slope of a line.

Sketch

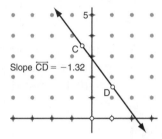

Step 1 In a new sketch, construct any line. Measure its slope by choosing **Measure | Slope**. A grid will appear. Click on a grid point and choose **Display | Line Width | Dotted**.

Step 2 Select one of the points on the line and drag this point to rotate the line. Observe the effect on its slope.

Step 3 Select the line and drag it around. Observe the effect on its slope.

Investigate

1. Which lines have a positive slope, and which have a negative slope?

2. What is the slope of a horizontal line?

3. How can you tell a steeper slope from a shallower slope?

4. What is the slope of a vertical line?

Investigation 2: Playing the Slope Game

Sketch

Play this game with a partner.

Step 1 Draw five different random lines in your sketch from Investigation 1. Make sure no labels are showing.

Step 2 Select all five lines and measure their slopes.

Step 3 Challenge your partner to match each measured slope with a line. Your partner is allowed to touch only measurements, to move them next to the lines they match. The lines and the points are "off limits" until all the measurements have been matched up with lines.

Step 4 The score is the number of slopes correctly matched with their lines. To check a match, drag one of the points that defines a line. If the slope is correctly matched to the line, its value will change.

Step 5 Switch roles, remove labels, scramble the lines, and play the game again. Add more lines to make the game more challenging.

(continued)

Step 6 Record your total scores after at least one complete round of the Slope Game.

Investigation 3: Calculating the Slope of a Line

Sketch

Step 1 Open the sketch **Slope of a Line.gsp.** Make sure you understand all the measurements showing in the sketch.

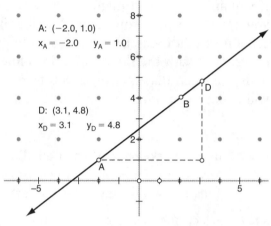

Step 2 Calculate the vertical change, or change in y, between point D and point A, using only the calculator and the measurements already showing in your sketch. Do not make any new measurements. This change is often called the **rise.**

Step 3 Calculate the horizontal change, or change in x, between point D and point A, using only the calculator and the measurements already showing in your sketch. This change is often called the **run.**

Step 4 Use the calculator to divide the rise by the run.

Investigate

1. Drag point D and observe your ratio $\frac{rise}{run}$. Record your observations.

2. Drag point A and point B until the line is horizontal. Describe the ratio $\frac{rise}{run}$ for a horizontal line.

3. Drag point A and point B until the line is vertical. Describe the ratio $\frac{rise}{run}$ for a vertical line.

4. Describe the line when the ratio $\frac{rise}{run}$ is negative.

5. Finally, measure the slope of your line and make a conjecture about how to calculate the slope of a line using coordinates.

6. Now you can generalize your conjecture using other variables. Suppose that one point on the line has coordinates $\left(x_1, y_1\right)$ and another has coordinates $\left(x_2, y_2\right)$. Find the slope of the line using these four variables and write your answers as part of a conjecture (Slope Formula).

EXPLORE MORE

In a new sketch, construct a line segment. Calculate the slope of the segment using only the coordinates of the endpoints. (Choose **Abscissa(x)** and **Ordinate(y)** from the Measure menu to find the coordinates.) Check your conjecture by calculating the slope using the Measure menu. Drag an endpoint of the segment and report on the results of your calculations.

Lesson 3.2 • Constructing Perpendicular Bisectors

The **perpendicular bisector** of a segment is the line that divides the segment into two congruent parts (bisects it) and that is also perpendicular to the line segment. In this activity you'll construct a perpendicular bisector using only Sketchpad's freehand tools. As you do so, you'll investigate properties of perpendicular bisectors.

Investigation 1: The Perpendicular Bisector Conjecture

Sketch

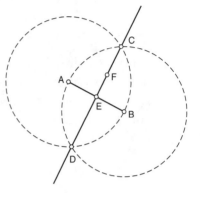

Step 1   Open a new sketch. Construct $\overline{AB}$.

Step 2   Construct a circle by starting at center point A and releasing the mouse with the cursor positioned at point B. Point B will then control the circle's radius.

Step 3   Construct a circle from center point B to radius control point A.

Step 4   Construct $\overleftrightarrow{CD}$, where C and D are the points of intersection of the circles.

Step 5   Construct point E, the point of intersection of $\overline{AB}$ and $\overleftrightarrow{CD}$.

Step 6   Construct F as a point on $\overleftrightarrow{CD}$.

Step 7   Hide the circles.

Step 8   Select points A and F and choose **Measure | Distance.** Then measure BF.

Investigate

1. Line CD is the perpendicular bisector of $\overline{AB}$. Drag points A and B. What's special about point E?

2. Drag point F up and down the line. What can you say about any point on a segment's perpendicular bisector? Write a conjecture (Perpendicular Bisector Conjecture).

Investigation 2: Is the Converse True?

Next you'll investigate the Converse of the Perpendicular Bisector Conjecture.

Sketch

Step 1   Continuing in the same sketch, construct point G, not on any object.

Step 2   Measure the distances from G to points A and B.

GA = 1.29 cm
GB = 2.24 cm

(continued)

Investigate

1. If a point is not on the perpendicular bisector of a segment, is it equidistant from the segment's endpoints?

2. Drag point *G* until it is equidistant (or as close to equidistant as you can get) from points *A* and *B*. Find several locations for point *G* such that *GA* = *GB*. What do you notice about every such location? Write the Converse of the Perpendicular Bisector Conjecture.

Explore more

1. Open a new sketch. Construct a segment and come up with a shortcut for constructing a perpendicular bisector using the Construct menu. Describe how you did it.

2. Construct a line *AB* and a point *C* not on the line. Double-click the line to mark it as a mirror for reflection. Select point *C* and choose **Transform | Reflect.** Construct segment *CC'*. Drag different parts of your sketch. How are $\overleftrightarrow{AB}$ and $\overline{CC'}$ related?

Lesson 3.3 • Medians and Altitudes

In this demonstration, you will observe properties of two triangle segments and write their definitions.

Sketch

Step 1 Open the sketch **Triangle Segments Demo.gsp**. △*ABC* has no special constraints here.

Step 2 Drag points *A*, *B*, and *C* and observe how segments *BE* and *BD* behave.

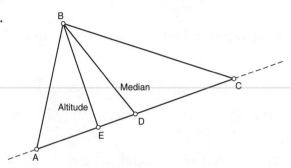

Investigate

1. Segment *BD* is a **median.** What do you think is the definition of *median of a triangle*? Make measurements to test or confirm your guess.

2. Segment *BE* is an **altitude.** When does $\overline{BE}$ fall outside the triangle? When does it fall inside the triangle?

3. Define *altitude of a triangle.*

4. How many medians does a triangle have? How many altitudes?

EXPLORE MORE

In a new sketch, construct a triangle with an altitude that stays an altitude no matter how you drag the triangle. Once you've figured out how to do it, construct the other two altitudes, too. Is it possible for exactly one altitude to fall outside the triangle? Exactly two? All three? Explain.

Lesson 3.3 • Constructing Perpendiculars to a Line

Measuring the distance between two points is easy, but how do you measure the distance between a point and a line? There are many different distances, depending on what point you measure to on the line. What's the shortest distance? That's what you'll investigate in this activity.

Investigation: Finding the Right Line

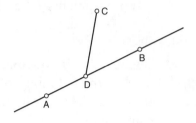

Sketch

Step 1   Open a new sketch. Construct $\overleftrightarrow{AB}$.

Step 2   Construct $\overline{CD}$, where point C is not on $\overleftrightarrow{AB}$ and point D is on $\overleftrightarrow{AB}$.

Step 3   Select point C and $\overleftrightarrow{AB}$ and choose **Measure | Distance.**

Step 4   Measure CD.

Investigate

1. Which is greater, CD or the distance from point C to $\overleftrightarrow{AB}$?

2. When you use Sketchpad to measure the distance from a point to a line, it gives the shortest distance. To discover what that shortest distance is, drag point D until the distance CD is as small as you can make it. It should be approximately equal to the distance from C to $\overleftrightarrow{AB}$. Select point C and $\overleftrightarrow{AB}$ and choose **Construct | Perpendicular Line.** What can you say about the shortest distance from a point to a line? Write a conjecture (Shortest Distance Conjecture).

Explore More

There's a sewage treatment plant at the point where two rivers meet. You want to build a house near the two rivers (upstream, naturally, from the sewage plant), but you want the house to be at least five miles from the sewage plant. You visit each of the rivers to go fishing about the same number of times, but, being lazy, you want to minimize the amount of walking you do. (You want the sum of the distances from your house to the two rivers to be minimal.) Where should you build your house?

Here is a model of the rivers and plant. Reconstruct this model in a new sketch, and investigate possible locations for the house.

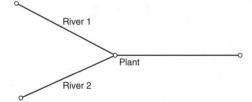

Discovering Geometry with The Geometer's Sketchpad
©2008 Key Curriculum Press

Lesson 3.4 • Constructing Angle Bisectors

An angle bisector is a ray that has its endpoint at the vertex of the angle and that divides the angle into two congruent angles. In this activity you'll investigate a special property of points on an angle bisector.

Investigation: The Angle Bisector Conjecture

Sketch

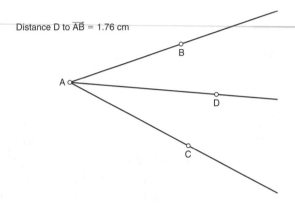

Distance D to $\overline{AB}$ = 1.76 cm

Step 1 In a new sketch, choose the **Ray** tool and draw $\vec{AB}$ and $\vec{AC}$. (To get the **Ray** tool, press and hold the **Straightedge** tool button.)

Step 2 Select, in order, points *B*, *A*, and *C* and choose **Construct | Angle Bisector.**

Step 3 Construct point *D* on the angle bisector.

Step 4 Select point *D* and $\vec{AB}$ and choose **Measure | Distance.**

Step 5 Measure the distance from point *D* to $\vec{AC}$.

Investigate

1. To confirm that $\vec{AD}$ bisects $\angle BAC$, measure angles *BAD* and *DAC*. Drag point *A*, *B*, or *C* to change $\angle BAC$. How do the angle measures compare?

2. Drag point *D* and observe the distances from point *D* to the two sides of the angle. Write a conjecture about any point on the bisector of an angle (Angle Bisector Conjecture).

EXPLORE MORE

1. In a new sketch, construct rays *AB* and *AC*. Double-click on $\vec{AC}$ to mark it as a reflection mirror. Then select $\vec{AB}$ and choose **Transform | Reflect.** Drag different points in your sketch. How are $\vec{AB}$ and $\vec{AC}$ related?

2. Write the Converse of the Angle Bisector Conjecture. Is the converse true? Explain how to support your answer with Sketchpad.

3. Construct an angle bisector using only Sketchpad's freehand tools—without the Construct or Transform menus.

Using Your Algebra Skills 3 • Slopes of Parallel and Perpendicular Lines

You have learned how to find the slope of any line or segment. In this activity you'll discover the relationships between slopes of parallel lines and between slopes of perpendicular lines.

Investigation 1: Lines with Equal Slopes

Sketch

Step 1 In a new sketch, construct lines AB and CD. Also construct their point of intersection, E.

Step 2 Measure $\angle CEA$.

Step 3 Measure the slopes of $\overleftrightarrow{AB}$ and $\overleftrightarrow{CD}$.

$m\angle CEA = 147.01°$

Investigate

1. Drag point D to change the direction of $\overleftrightarrow{CD}$. Observe your measurements. As the measure of $\angle CEA$ approaches 0°, point E will go off the screen and the lines will approach being parallel. You might be able to make the lines exactly parallel, in which case the angle will cease to exist and its measurement will disappear. Drag D to make the slope measurements equal. What can you conclude about two lines that have equal slopes?

Investigation 2: Parallel Lines

Sketch

Step 1 In the same sketch, drag point D so the slopes of $\overleftrightarrow{AB}$ and $\overleftrightarrow{CD}$ are no longer equal. Now construct a new line through C parallel to $\overleftrightarrow{AB}$.

Step 2 Measure the slope of the new line.

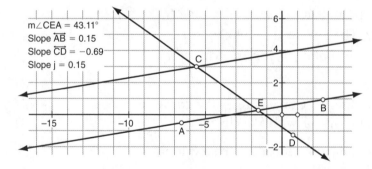

$m\angle CEA = 43.11°$
Slope $\overline{AB} = 0.15$
Slope $\overline{CD} = -0.69$
Slope j $= 0.15$

Investigate

1. Drag point B and observe the slopes. What do you notice about the slopes of two parallel lines?

2. Write your observations about parallel lines and slopes as a conjecture (Parallel Slope Property).

(continued)

Investigation 3: Perpendicular Lines

Sketch

Step 1 In a new sketch, construct $\overleftrightarrow{AB}$.

Step 2 Construct point C not on $\overleftrightarrow{AB}$.

Step 3 Construct a line through C perpendicular to $\overleftrightarrow{AB}$.

Step 4 Measure the slope of each line.

Step 5 Calculate the product of the slopes. (Choose **Measure |
Calculate.** Click on the slope measurements in the sketch to
include them in your calculation.)

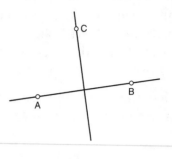

Investigate

1. Drag point B and observe the slopes and their product. If two lines are
perpendicular, what is the relationship between their slopes?

Investigation 4: When Are Two Lines Perpendicular?

This sketch is similar to the one you made in Investigation 1.

Sketch

Step 1 In a new sketch, construct lines AB and CD.
Also construct their point of intersection, E.

Step 2 Measure $\angle CEA$.

Step 3 Measure the slopes of $\overleftrightarrow{AB}$ and $\overleftrightarrow{CD}$.

Step 4 Calculate the product of the slopes.

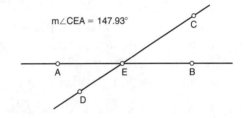

Investigate

1. Drag D until the product of the two slopes equals -1. (This could be
hard to do if your measurements are very precise. You can change the
precision by choosing **Edit | Preferences.**) Observe the measure $\angle CEA$.
What do you notice about lines with slopes whose product is -1?

2. Combine your observations from the last two investigations to write a
conjecture about the slopes of perpendicular lines (Perpendicular
Slope Property).

Exploration • Perspective Drawing

Even though a piece of paper or a computer screen is flat, you can draw figures that appear three-dimensional by drawing in perspective. In three dimensions, objects that are farther away appear smaller to us. Perspective drawing takes advantage of this principle to make flat drawings appear to have depth.

Follow these steps to draw a box with two-point perspective. Labels are shown to clarify these directions, but you probably won't want labels on your drawing.

Activity: Boxes in Space

Sketch

Step 1 Open a new sketch. Construct a long horizontal segment AB near the top of the window. (To make the segment exactly horizontal, hold down the Shift key while constructing it.) This will be your **horizon line,** and its endpoints will be the **vanishing points** of your perspective box.

Step 2 Construct point C below $\overline{AB}$. Select both C and $\overline{AB}$, and choose **Construct | Perpendicular Line.**

Step 3 Construct point D above point C on the line you constructed in Step 2. Hide the perpendicular line, then construct $\overline{CD}$. Change its line width to dashed using the Display menu.

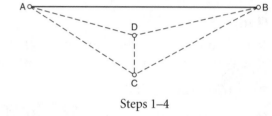

Steps 1–4

Step 4 Construct $\overline{CA}$, $\overline{DA}$, $\overline{CB}$, and $\overline{DB}$.

Step 5 Construct point E on $\overline{CA}$ and point F on $\overline{CB}$.

Step 6 Select points E and F and segment CD and choose **Construct | Parallel Line** to construct two lines parallel to $\overline{CD}$.

Step 7 Construct $\overline{GB}$ and $\overline{HA}$, where points G and H are the new points of intersection with $\overline{DA}$ and $\overline{DB}$.

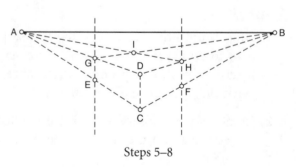

Steps 5–8

Step 8 Construct point I at the point of intersection of $\overline{GB}$ and $\overline{HA}$.

(continued)

Discovering Geometry with The Geometer's Sketchpad
©2008 Key Curriculum Press

Step 9 Change the line width of $\overline{CD}$ to thick; then construct $\overline{GI}$, $\overline{IH}$, $\overline{HF}$, $\overline{FC}$, $\overline{CE}$, $\overline{EG}$, $\overline{GD}$, and $\overline{DH}$.

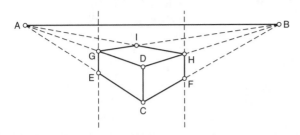

Step 10 Hide all the dashed lines and segments to leave just your box and the horizon line.

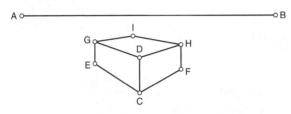

Step 11 Try moving various parts of your box, your horizon segment, and the vanishing points. If you move the front edge of your box above the horizon segment, you'll discover that you haven't created the bottom of your box. Continue sketching to construct the missing edges as shown. (You might start by constructing a dashed segment from point E to point B.)

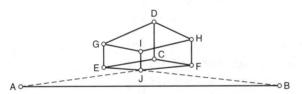

Step 12 Hide unwanted points and segments. (Points A, B, C, D, E, and F will be the only points that can be dragged.)

Investigate

Write a description of what happens as you move the horizon line and vanishing points. How can you look at the bottom of the box? What's the position of the viewer when the horizon line is above the box? What effect does moving the vanishing points farther apart have on the view of the box?

Lesson 3.7 • Constructing Points of Concurrency

In these three investigations you'll discover some properties of angle bisectors, perpendicular bisectors, and altitudes in a triangle.

Investigation 1: Angle Bisectors in a Triangle

Sketch

Step 1 In a new sketch, construct △*ABC*.

Step 2 Select points *B*, *A*, and *C*, in that order, and choose **Construct | Angle Bisector** to bisect ∠*A*.

Step 3 Construct the bisector of ∠*B*.

Step 4 Construct point *D* where these two rays intersect.

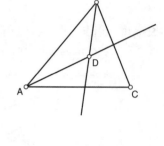

Investigate

1. Construct the bisector of ∠*C*. What do you notice about this third angle bisector? Drag the vertices of the triangle to see if this is always true.

2. If you were blindfolded and drew three lines on a piece of paper, do you think they would intersect in a single point? When lines that lie in the same plane *do* intersect in a single point, they're said to be **concurrent.** Using the word *concurrent*, write a conjecture about the three angle bisectors of a triangle (Angle Bisector Concurrency Conjecture).

3. The point of concurrency of the angle bisectors in a triangle is called the **incenter.** Select point *D* and $\overline{AB}$ and choose **Measure | Distance.** Also measure the distances from point *D* to the other two sides. Drag parts of the triangle; then write a conjecture about the incenter of a triangle (Incenter Conjecture).

Sketch

Step 5 Continuing in the same sketch, hide the rays.

Step 6 Double-click on the label *D*, and change it to *I*, for incenter. Check the box Use Label in Custom Tools.

Step 7 Select the entire figure, but not the measurements. Press and hold the **Custom** tools icon to display the Custom Tools menu. Choose **Create New Tool,** and name the tool **Incenter.**

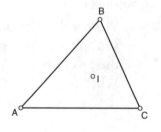

Step 8 Save your sketch as instructed by your teacher. You can use the **Incenter** tool in other sketches whenever this one is open. You'll need this tool for the Explore More and for a later Exploration.

(continued)

Investigation 2: Perpendicular Bisectors in a Triangle

Sketch

Step 1   Open a new sketch.

Step 2   Construct △*ABC* and drag it so that it appears to be acute.

Step 3   Construct points *D* and *E*, the midpoints of $\overline{AB}$ and $\overline{AC}$.

Step 4   To construct the perpendicular bisector of $\overline{AB}$, select point *D* and $\overline{AB}$ and choose **Construct | Perpendicular Line.**

Step 5   Construct the perpendicular bisector of $\overline{AC}$.

Step 6   Construct point *F* where these two perpendicular bisectors intersect, and then construct the perpendicular bisector of $\overline{BC}$.

Investigate

1. Write a conjecture about the three perpendicular bisectors of a triangle (Perpendicular Bisector Concurrency Conjecture). Include in your conjecture any differences you observe between acute and obtuse triangles.

2. The point of concurrency of the perpendicular bisectors of a triangle is called the **circumcenter.** Measure distances from the circumcenter to each of the three vertices of the triangle. Drag parts of the triangle; then write a conjecture about the circumcenter of a triangle (Circumcenter Conjecture).

Sketch

Step 7   Hide the lines and midpoints.

Step 8   Change the label of point *F* to *Ci*, for circumcenter. Check the box Use Label in Custom Tools.

Step 9   Select the entire figure except for the measurements. Choose **Create New Tool** from the Custom Tools menu. Name the tool **Circumcenter.**

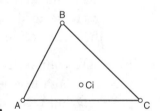

Step 10   Save your sketch as instructed by your teacher. You can use the tool in other sketches whenever this one is open. You'll need this tool for the Explore More and for a later Exploration.

Investigation 3: Altitudes in a Triangle

Sketch

Step 1   Open a new sketch.

Step 2   Construct △*ABC* and drag it so that it appears acute.

Step 3   Select $\overline{AC}$ and point *B* and choose **Construct | Perpendicular Line.** This line contains an altitude of △*ABC*.

Step 4   Construct a line through point *A* that contains an altitude.

Step 5   Construct point *D*, the point of intersection of these two lines, and then construct the line containing the third altitude in △*ABC*, through point *C*.

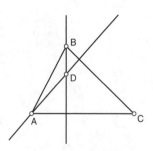

(continued)

Investigate

1. Write a conjecture about the three altitudes (or the lines containing the altitudes) of a triangle (Altitude Concurrency Conjecture). The point of concurrency is called the **orthocenter.** Include in your conjecture what you observe about the orthocenter in acute and obtuse triangles.

Sketch

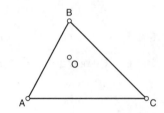

Step 6 Continuing in the same sketch, hide the lines.

Step 7 Change the label of point *D* to *O*, for orthocenter. Check the box Use Label in Custom Tools.

Step 8 Select the entire figure. Choose **Create New Tool** from the Custom Tools menu. Name the tool **Orthocenter.**

Step 9 Save your sketch, as instructed by your teacher. You can use the tool in other sketches whenever this one is open. You'll need this tool for a later Exploration.

EXPLORE MORE

1. Be sure your sketch containing the **Custom** tool **Circumcenter** is open. Now open a new sketch and select **Circumcenter** from the Custom Tools menu. As you construct three points, the triangle and its circumcenter will appear. Now choose the **Compass** tool and draw a circle centered at the circumcenter, dragging to one of the three vertices of the triangle. A circle that passes through each vertex of a polygon is a **circumscribed circle.** Explain why a circumscribed circle is centered at the circumcenter of a triangle.

2. Be sure your sketch containing the **Custom** tool **Incenter** is open. Now open a new sketch and choose **Incenter** from the Custom Tools menu. Construct a circle centered at the incenter and drag it out until it just touches one of the three sides of the triangle. A circle that touches each side of a polygon at exactly one point is an **inscribed circle.** Explain why a circle inscribed in a triangle is centered at the incenter. See whether you can construct an inscribed circle that stays inscribed no matter how you drag the triangle.

Lessons 3.7 and 3.8 • Points of Concurrency

In this demonstration you'll discover properties of several remarkable points associated with a triangle.

Medians

Sketch

Step 1 Open the sketch **Triangle Points Demo.gsp** to the page Points of Concurrency.

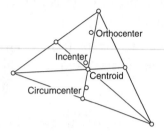

Step 2 Press *Show Medians.* You'll see the medians intersecting in a single point. This point of concurrency is called the **centroid.**

Step 3 Drag a vertex of the triangle and observe the medians.

Investigate

1. Do the medians always intersect in a single point, no matter what shape the triangle is?

2. Press *Show Distance Measurements.* Watch the measurements as you drag. Into what ratio does the centroid divide each median?

Altitudes

Sketch

Step 4 Press *Hide Medians.*

Step 5 Press *Show Altitudes.* You'll see three lines that contain the altitudes of the triangle. These lines intersect in a point of concurrency called the **orthocenter.**

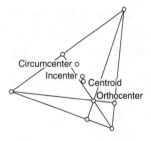

Step 6 Drag a vertex of the triangle and observe the altitudes.

Investigate

3. Do the altitudes always intersect in a single point, no matter what shape the triangle is?

4. Describe triangles in which the orthocenter falls inside, outside, and on the triangle. On what point does the orthocenter fall when it falls on the triangle?

(continued)

Angle Bisectors

Sketch

Step 7   Press *Hide Altitudes.*

Step 8   Press *Show Angle Bisectors.* You'll see the three
angle bisectors intersecting in a single point.
This point of concurrency is called the
incenter. The incenter is the center of the
inscribed circle.

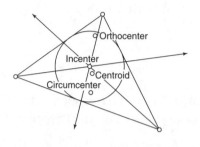

Step 9   Drag a vertex of the triangle and observe
the angle bisectors and the inscribed circle.

Investigate

5. Do the angle bisectors always intersect in a single point, no matter
what shape the triangle is?

6. Explain why the incenter is the center of the inscribed circle.
(Think about the properties of all points on an angle bisector.)

Perpendicular Bisectors

Sketch

Step 10   Press *Hide Angle Bisectors.*

Step 11   Press *Show Perpendicular Bisectors.* You'll see the
perpendicular bisectors of the three sides of the
triangle intersecting in a single point. This point
of concurrency is called the **circumcenter.**
The circumcenter is the center of the
circumscribed circle.

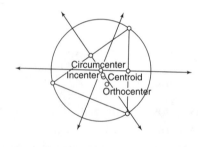

Step 12   Drag a vertex of the triangle and observe the perpendicular bisectors
and the circumscribed circle.

Investigate

7. Do the perpendicular bisectors always intersect in a single point, no
matter what shape the triangle is?

8. Describe triangles in which the circumcenter falls inside, outside, and
on the triangle. On what point does the circumcenter fall when it falls
on the triangle?

9. Explain why the circumcenter is the center of the circumscribed circle.
(Think about properties of all points on perpendicular bisectors.)

Lesson 3.7 • The Nine-Point Circle

Extension

In 1820, French mathematicians Charles Brianchon (1785–1864) and
Jean Victor Poncelet (1788–1867) published a paper that contained the
proof of the following statement: "The circle that passes through the feet
of the perpendiculars, dropped from the vertices of any triangle on the
sides opposite them, passes also through the midpoints of these sides and
through the midpoints of the segments that join the vertices to the point
of intersection of the perpendiculars."

Did you catch all of that? This circle is called the **nine-point circle,** and
it has many special properties. In this extension you'll use The Geometer's
Sketchpad to create and explore the nine-point circle.

Investigation: Constructing the Nine-Point Circle

Sketch

Step 1   In a new sketch, construct a large scalene triangle.
Label it △ABC.

Step 2   Measure the angles of the triangle. To measure an
angle, select three points on the angle, with the
vertex as the second selection.

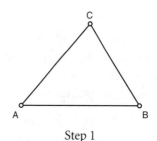

Step 1

Step 3   Select $\overline{AB}$ and point C and choose **Construct |
Perpendicular Line.** Construct the other two lines
containing the altitudes in the same way.

Step 4   Label the points of intersection with the sides
as P_1, P_2, and P_3. Label the orthocenter R. Use
brackets to enter subscripts. For example, to
get P_1 enter $P[1]$.

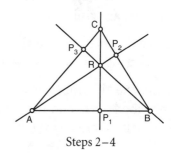

Steps 2–4

Step 5   Construct the midpoint of each side of the triangle
by selecting each side and choosing **Construct |
Midpoint.** Label the midpoint of $\overline{AB}$ as P_4, the
midpoint of $\overline{BC}$ as P_5, and the midpoint of $\overline{AC}$
as P_6.

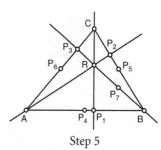

Step 5

Step 6   Construct $\overline{BR}$, $\overline{CR}$, and $\overline{AR}$, and then construct
their midpoints. Label the midpoint of $\overline{BR}$ as P_7,
the midpoint of $\overline{CR}$ as P_8, and the midpoint of $\overline{AR}$
as P_9.

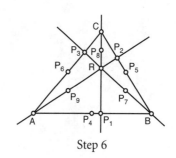

Step 6

(continued)

Step 7   Construct line segments connecting point P_4 to P_8, point P_5 to P_9, and point P_6 to P_7. All the segments should intersect in one point. Construct the intersection by clicking on it, and label it point O.

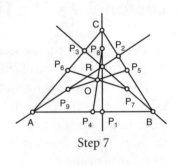

Step 7

Step 8   Construct a circle with center at point O and radius OP_1. The circle should pass through all nine points: P_1, P_2, P_3, P_4, P_5, P_6, P_7, P_8, and P_9.

Step 9   Drag the triangle. Do all nine points always stay on the circle?

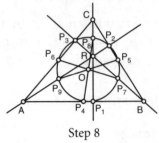

Step 8

Investigate

1. As you drag the triangle, you may observe that points on the nine-point circle sometimes coincide. Make two of the nine points coincide so that only eight points are visible. What kind of triangle is this? Which two points coincide?

2. Describe all the triangles you can find in which fewer than eight of the points on the nine-point circle are visible. In each case, describe how many points are visible and which points coincide.

3. Construct the incenter and the inscribed circle. Drag the triangle. How are the inscribed circle and the nine-point circle related?

4. Construct the circumcenter and the circumscribed circle. How are the circumscribed circle and the nine-point circle related? (*Hint:* You may want to make some measurements.)

Lesson 3.8 • The Centroid

In Lesson 3.7, you discovered that the three angle bisectors in a triangle are concurrent, as are the three perpendicular bisectors and the three altitudes. Here you'll investigate the three medians in a triangle.

Investigation 1: Conjecture About Medians

Sketch

Step 1 In a new sketch, construct $\triangle ABC$.

Step 2 Construct the midpoint D of $\overline{AC}$ and median $\overline{BD}$.

Step 3 Construct the midpoint E of $\overline{AB}$ and median $\overline{CE}$.

Step 4 Construct point F where these medians intersect, and then construct the third median, from point A to $\overline{BC}$.

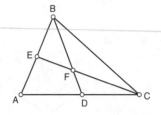

Investigate

1. Write a conjecture about the three medians of a triangle (Median Concurrency Conjecture).

Investigation 2: The Centroid Conjecture

Sketch

Step 1 Change the label of point F to Ce, for centroid. Before clicking OK in the dialog box, check Use Label in Custom Tools. The **centroid** is the point of concurrency of the medians.

Step 2 Measure the distance from B to Ce and the distance from Ce to D.

Step 3 Drag vertices of $\triangle ABC$. Look for a relationship between BCe and CeD.

Step 4 Select the distance measurements and choose **Graph | Tabulate.**

Step 5 Move a vertex of the triangle; then double-click inside the table to add another entry.

Investigate

1. Keep changing the triangle and adding entries to your table until you find a relationship between the distances BCe and CeD that holds for any triangle. Write a conjecture (Centroid Conjecture).

Sketch

Step 6 In the same sketch, hide the midpoints and medians of $\triangle ABC$, but don't hide the centroid.

Step 7 Select the entire triangle, including the centroid. Choose **Create New Tool** from the Custom Tools menu. Name the tool **Centroid.** Save your sketch as instructed by your teacher. You'll need this tool for the upcoming Exploration.

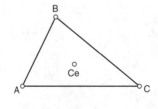

Exploration • The Euler Segment

Sketch

Step 1 Open the sketch **Triangle Points Demo.gsp** to the page Euler Segment.

Step 2 Press *Show Euler Segment.* You'll see the four points of concurrency you've studied so far and a segment connecting three of them. Drag a vertex and observe the Euler segment.

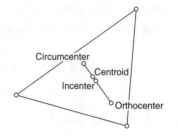

Investigate

1. Which point of concurrency is not usually on the Euler segment?

2. Are the endpoints of the Euler segment always the same two points? If so, what points are they?

3. What point is on the Euler segment but is not an endpoint? Press *Show Distances.* How does this point divide the Euler segment?

4. In what kind of triangle are all four points of concurrency on the Euler segment?

5. In what kind of triangle do all four points of concurrency coincide?

6. Is it possible for two or three of the points of concurrency to coincide without the fourth joining in?

7. In what kind of triangle do the endpoints of the Euler segment fall on the triangle? At what points do these endpoints fall?

Exploration • The Euler Line

In this activity you'll look for a relationship among four points of concurrency: the incenter, the circumcenter, the orthocenter, and the centroid. You'll need the **Custom** tools you made in Lessons 3.7 and 3.8. You'll see how tools of complicated constructions make it easy to repeat those constructions any time you want.

Activity: Three Out of Four

Sketch

Step 1 Open a new sketch.

Step 2 Be sure your sketches containing the four **Custom** tools are open.

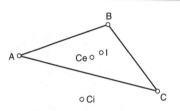

Step 3 Choose **Centroid** from the Custom Tools menu.

Step 4 Click three times to construct △ABC and its centroid.

Step 5 Choose the **Custom** tool **Incenter** and construct the incenter of △ABC by clicking on the triangle's vertices.

Step 6 Choose the **Custom** tool **Circumcenter** and construct the circumcenter of △ABC.

Step 7 Choose the **Custom** tool **Orthocenter** and construct the orthocenter of △ABC.

Investigate

1. The four points of concurrency you've constructed in this triangle all have special properties that you discovered earlier. Three of these four points are collinear. Drag the triangle to see which three these are. The line they lie on is called the **Euler line.** Which points lie on the Euler line? Write a conjecture (Euler Line Conjecture).

2. When all four points are collinear, what kind of triangle do you have?

3. When all four points are coincident (at the same place), what kind of triangle do you have?

4. Mess up the triangle, then construct a segment connecting two of the three points on the Euler line and passing through the third. This is the **Euler segment.** What are its endpoints? What is the other point on the Euler segment?

5. The point that's not an endpoint divides the Euler segment into two parts. Measure the distances between the endpoints of each of these two parts. Look for a relationship between these distances and write a conjecture (Euler Segment Conjecture).

You have studied four triangle points of concurrency in Chapter 3. Would you be surprised to learn that there are hundreds more? In this extension you'll use The Geometer's Sketchpad to construct and explore one of these other points.

An **excircle** of a triangle is a circle that is tangent to a side and to lines through the two adjacent sides. A triangle has only one inscribed circle, but it has three excircles.

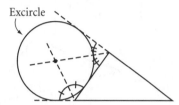

The center of an excircle lies on the bisectors of two adjacent exterior angles of the triangle. This will be the starting point of your construction.

Investigation 1: The Nagel Point

Sketch

Step 1   In a new sketch, construct $\triangle ABC$.

Step 2   Use the **Ray** tool to construct $\overrightarrow{AB}$ and $\overrightarrow{AC}$. Construct point D on $\overrightarrow{AB}$ and point E on $\overrightarrow{AC}$.

Step 3   Select, in order, points D, B, and C and choose **Construct | Angle Bisector.** Construct the bisector of $\angle ECB$.

Step 4   Construct the intersection H of the two angle bisectors by clicking on it with the **Arrow** tool. Select H and $\overline{BC}$ and choose **Construct | Perpendicular Line.** Construct the point of intersection I of this line with $\overline{BC}$.

Step 5   Construct a circle with center H through point I. This is the excircle tangent to $\overline{BC}$. Select the rays and lines and choose **Display | Line Width | Dashed.**

Step 6   Construct $\overline{AI}$, and change its line width to thin and its color to orange using the Display menu. Hide the angle bisectors and perpendicular bisector.

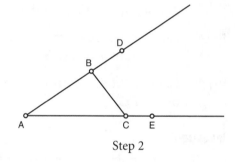

Step 2

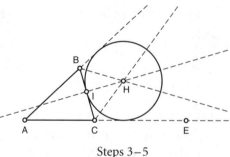

Steps 3–5

(continued)

Discovering Geometry with The Geometer's Sketchpad
©2008 Key Curriculum Press

Chapter 3 Review • The Nagel Segment (continued)

Step 7 Repeat Steps 2–6 to create excircles tangent to $\overline{AB}$ and $\overline{AC}$.

Step 8 Select all points (click on the **Point** tool and choose **Edit | Select All Points**). Then choose **Display | Hide Labels.**

Step 9 Select two of the orange segments and construct their intersection point. Label it *N*.

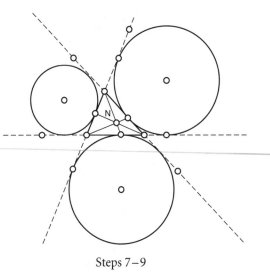

Steps 7–9

Investigate

1. Drag the triangle and observe the three orange segments. Make a conjecture based on your observations.

2. The point of concurrency of the three segments, point *N* in your sketch, is called the **Nagel point.** Drag the triangle. Is the Nagel point ever outside the triangle? On the triangle? Explain why.

Investigation 2: The Nagel Segment

Sketch

Step 1 Open the sketch **Nagel Segment.gsp.**

Step 2 The sketch shows the Nagel point along with the four points of concurrency you have previously studied. Two of the points of concurrency are collinear with the Nagel point. Drag the triangle to confirm this.

Step 3 Construct a segment that connects two of the three collinear points and contains the third point. This segment is called the **Nagel segment.**

Investigate

1. Which points of concurrency are collinear with the Nagel point?

2. What are the endpoints of the Nagel segment? Are they always the endpoints?

3. Measure the distances from the middle point of concurrency on the Nagel segment to the endpoints. How are these distances related?

This sketch demonstrates a property of the angles of any triangle.
The sketch also demonstrates why this property holds.

Sketch

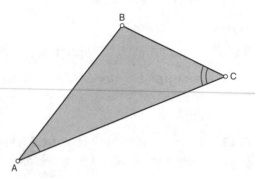

Step 1　Open the sketch **Triangle Sum Demo.gsp.**

Step 2　Drag each vertex of the triangle and observe
how the angle measures change.

Step 3　Press *Show Sum.*

Step 4　Drag each vertex again and observe the effect on
the sum.

Step 5　Press *Show Why,* then press each of the two
buttons that appear, observing the effects of
each button.

Step 6　Press *Reset,* change the triangle, and again press *Show Why.*

Investigate

1. What is the sum of any three angles that form a straight line?

2. What is the sum of the angle measures in any triangle?

3. Write a paragraph or two explaining how the *Show Why* button
demonstrates why the sum of the angle measures in a triangle is what
it is. Include diagrams with your explanation.

Lesson 4.1 • Triangle Sum Conjecture

In this activity, you'll investigate and make a conjecture about the sum of the measures of the angles in a triangle.

Investigation: The Triangle Sum

Sketch

Step 1 In a new sketch, construct △ABC.

Step 2 Measure ∠CAB, ∠CBA, and ∠ACB. Make sure that the vertex is the second point you select on each angle.

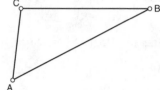

m∠CAB = 56.15°
m∠CBA = 26.97°
m∠ACB = 96.88°

Step 3 Use the calculator (choose **Measure | Calculate**) to calculate m∠CAB + m∠CBA + m∠ACB.

Investigate

1. Drag points A, B, and C. What do you observe about the sum of the three angles?

2. Write a conjecture about the sum of the three angles of a triangle (Triangle Sum Conjecture).

EXPLORE MORE

1. Construct a triangle, and construct a line through one vertex parallel to the opposite side.

   a. How do the three angles formed at the vertex compare with the angles in the triangle?

   b. Explain how the Triangle Sum Conjecture follows logically from the Parallel Lines Conjecture.

2. Select the three vertices and choose **Construct | Triangle Interior**. Select vertex A and then vertex C, and choose **Transform | Mark Vector**. Finally, select the interior of the triangle and choose **Transform | Translate**. The dialog box should indicate that you are translating by the marked vector from point A to point C. Press **Translate**.

   a. What would fill the space between your two triangles? Construct the midpoint of $\overline{BC}$, mark it as center, and rotate the interior of △ABC 180° about this point.

   b. What can you say about the three angles that now meet at point C?

   c. How does this confirm the Triangle Sum Conjecture?

3. Investigate angle sums in other polygons.

4. Find another way to demonstrate the Triangle Sum Conjecture.

Lesson 4.2 • Properties of Isosceles Triangles

In this activity you'll learn how to construct an **isosceles triangle** (a triangle with at least two sides the same length). Then you'll discover properties of isosceles triangles.

Investigation 1: Base Angles in an Isosceles Triangle

Sketch

Step 1 In a new sketch, construct a circle with center *A* and control point *B*.

Step 2 Construct radius *AB*.

Step 3 Construct point *C* on the circle, and then construct radius *AC*.

Step 4 Construct $\overline{BC}$.

Step 5 Hide circle *AB*.

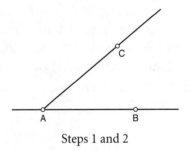

Investigate

1. Drag each vertex of your triangle. Explain why the triangle is always isosceles.

2. Measure $\angle ACB$ and $\angle ABC$. Make sure the vertex is the second point you select. Angles *ACB* and *ABC* are the **base angles** of the isosceles triangle. Angle *CAB* is the **vertex angle.** Drag the vertices of your triangle and observe the measures of $\angle ABC$ and $\angle ACB$. What do you observe about the measures?

3. Write a conjecture about the base angles of an isosceles triangle (Isosceles Triangle Conjecture).

Investigation 2: Is the Converse True?

In this sketch you will construct a triangle that has base angles of equal measure, then investigate the measures of the sides.

Sketch

Step 1 In a new sketch, construct $\overleftrightarrow{AB}$.

Step 2 Choose the **Ray** tool and construct $\overrightarrow{AC}$ to form acute $\angle CAB$.

Step 3 Mark $\angle CAB$ as an angle of rotation by selecting, in order, points *C*, *A*, and *B*, then choosing **Transform | Mark Angle.**

Step 4 Double-click on point *B* to mark it as a center for rotation.

Steps 1 and 2

(continued)

Step 5 Select $\overrightarrow{AB}$ and choose **Transform | Rotate.** Rotate $\overrightarrow{AB}$ by the marked angle.

Step 6 Construct the point of intersection *D* of this line and $\overleftrightarrow{AC}$.

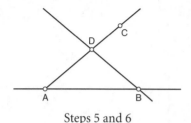

Steps 5 and 6

Step 7 Hide the ray and the two lines, and leave all of the points showing.

Step 8 Choose the **Segment** tool and construct △*ADB*.

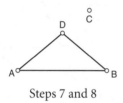

Steps 7 and 8

Investigate

1. Drag point *C* to change the measure of ∠*CAB*. What do you observe about △*ADB*?

2. Measure the sides of △*ADB* by selecting them and choosing **Measure | Length.** Drag point *C*. What do you observe about the lengths of $\overline{AD}$ and $\overline{BD}$?

3. What do you observe about a triangle that has two angles of equal measure? Write your findings as a conjecture (Converse of the Isosceles Triangle Conjecture).

EXPLORE MORE

Use Sketchpad to investigate the statement "If a triangle is equiangular, then it is equilateral" and its converse, "If a triangle is equilateral, then it is equiangular." Can you construct an equiangular triangle that is not equilateral? Can you construct an equilateral triangle that is not equiangular? Write a conjecture based on your investigation (Equilateral/Equiangular Triangle Conjecture).

Lesson 4.3 • Triangle Inequalities

In this investigation you'll discover relationships among the measures of the sides and angles in a triangle.

Investigation 1: What is the Shortest Path from *A* to *B*?

First, you'll determine whether you can construct a triangle from any three segments.

Sketch

Step 1 In a new sketch, construct a triangle.

Step 2 Display the segment labels, but not the point labels.

Step 3 Measure the lengths of the three sides by selecting them and choosing **Measure | Length.**

Step 4 Calculate the sum of any two side lengths by choosing **Measure | Calculate.** Click on each segment measurement that you want to include in your calculation.

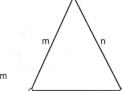

m = 1.925 cm
n = 1.941 cm
p = 1.729 cm
m + n = 3.865 cm

Investigate

1. Drag a vertex of the triangle to make the sum you calculated equal to the length of the third side. What happens to the triangle?

2. Is it possible for the sum of the lengths of any two sides of a triangle to be less than the length of the third side? Explain.

3. Summarize your findings as a conjecture about the sum of the lengths of two sides of a triangle (Triangle Inequality Conjecture).

Investigation 2: Where Are the Largest and Smallest Angles?

Sketch

Step 1 In your triangle sketch from Investigation 1, show the point labels and hide the segment labels.

Step 2 Measure ∠*A*, ∠*B*, and ∠*C*.

Step 3 Measure $\overline{AB}$, $\overline{BC}$, and $\overline{CA}$.

Investigate

1. Copy this chart onto your paper. Then drag the vertices of your triangle to help you fill in the chart with the name of the angle that has the greatest or least measure.

2. Write your findings as a conjecture (Side-Angle Inequality Conjecture).

Longest side	Largest angle	Shortest side	Smallest angle
$\overline{AB}$	∠*C*	$\overline{AB}$	
$\overline{AC}$		$\overline{AC}$	
$\overline{BC}$		$\overline{BC}$	

(continued)

Investigation 3: Exterior Angles of a Triangle

Here you will investigate the measure of the exterior angle of a triangle.

Sketch

Step 1 Construct ray $\overrightarrow{AB}$.

Step 2 Construct $\triangle ABC$.

Step 3 Construct point D on $\overrightarrow{AB}$ outside the triangle.

Step 4 Measure $\angle CAB$, $\angle ACB$, and $\angle CBD$.

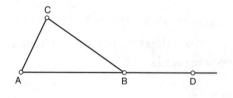

Investigate

1. Calculate the sum $\angle CAB + \angle ACB$. Drag point C. What do you observe? Write your findings as a conjecture (Triangle Exterior Angle Conjecture).

EXPLORE MORE

1. Can you form a quadrilateral from any four segments? What must be true about the four segments if they can form a quadrilateral? Investigate.

2. Investigate inequalities in the medians or altitudes of a triangle. Write your findings or conjectures.

3. How might you translate and rotate the interior of $\triangle ABC$ to show how the angles at A and C fit into the exterior angle at B?

Lesson 4.4 • Are There Congruence Shortcuts?

In this lesson you will investigate three possible congruence shortcuts.

Investigation 1: Is SSS a Congruence Shortcut?

If the three sides in one triangle are congruent to three sides in another triangle (SSS), must the two triangles be congruent?

Sketch

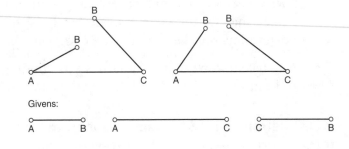

Step 1 Open the sketch **Congruence Shortcuts.gsp** to the page SSS.

Step 2 Drag the points labeled *B* in the broken triangle on the left so that they coincide to form a triangle.

Step 3 In the broken triangle on the right, try to make the points labeled *B* coincide so that the triangle formed is not congruent to the triangle on the left.

Step 4 Change the length of one or more of the given sides (the free segments below the triangles) and try the experiment again.

Investigate

1. Can you make triangles with different sizes or shapes with one set of three sides?

2. If you are given two triangles with three pairs of congruent sides, is that enough information to determine that the triangles are congruent?

3. Write a conjecture that summarizes your findings (SSS Congruence Conjecture).

Investigation 2: Is SAS a Congruence Shortcut?

If the two sides and the angle between them in one triangle are congruent to two sides and the angle between them in another triangle (SAS), must the two triangles be congruent?

Sketch

Step 1 Go to the page SAS.

Step 2 Drag the point labeled *B (drag)* in the broken triangle on the left so that it coincides with the other point *B* to form a triangle.

Step 3 In the broken triangle on the right, try to make the points labeled *B* coincide so that the triangle formed is not congruent to the triangle on the left.

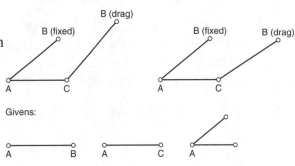

(continued)

Step 4 Change the length of one or more of the given sides or the measure of the given angle (the free segments and angle below the triangles) and try the experiment again.

Investigate

1. Can you make two triangles with different sizes or shapes given the two sides and the angle between them?

2. If you are given two triangles such that two sides and the angle between them in one triangle are congruent to two sides and the angle between them in the other triangle (SAS), is that enough information to determine that the triangles are congruent?

3. Write a conjecture that summarizes your findings (SAS Congruence Conjecture).

Investigation 3: Is SSA a Congruence Shortcut?

If the two sides and an angle not between them in one triangle are congruent to two sides and an angle not between them in another triangle (SSA), must the two triangles be congruent?

Sketch

Step 1 Go to the page SSA.

Step 2 Drag the points labeled *B* in the broken triangle on the left so that they coincide to form a triangle.

Step 3 In the broken triangle on the right, try to make the points labeled *B* coincide so that the triangle formed is not congruent to the triangle on the left.

Step 4 Change the length of one or more of the given sides or the measure of the given angle (the free segments and angle below the triangles) and try the experiment again.

Investigate

1. Can you form two triangles with different sizes or shapes given two sides and an angle not between them?

2. If you are given two triangles such that two sides and an angle not between them in one triangle are congruent to two sides and an angle not between them in the other triangle (SSA), is that enough information to determine that the triangles are congruent?

3. Summarize your findings.

Lesson 4.5 • Are There Other Congruence Shortcuts?

In this investigation you will investigate two other potential congruence shortcuts.

Investigation 1: Is ASA a Congruence Shortcut?

If two angles and the side between them in one triangle are congruent to two angles and the side between them in another triangle (ASA), must the two triangles be congruent?

Sketch

Step 1 Open the sketch **Congruence Shortcuts.gsp** to the page ASA.

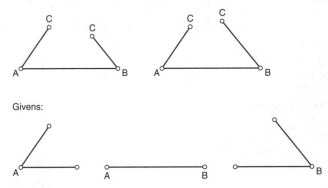

Givens:

Step 2 Drag the points labeled *C* in the broken triangle on the left so that they coincide to form a triangle.

Step 3 In the broken triangle on the right, try to make the points labeled *C* coincide so that the triangle formed is not congruent to the triangle on the left.

Step 4 Change the measure of one or more of the given angles or the given side (the angles and segment below the triangles) and try the experiment again.

Investigate

1. Can you form two triangles with different sizes or shapes given the two angles and the side between them?

2. If you are given two triangles such that two angles and the side between them in one triangle are congruent to two angles and the side between them in another triangle (ASA), is that enough information to determine that the triangles are congruent?

3. Write a conjecture that summarizes your findings (ASA Congruence Conjecture).

(continued)

Investigation 2: Is AAA a Congruence Shortcut?

If the three angles of one triangle are congruent to the three angles in another triangle (AAA), must the two triangles be congruent?

Sketch

Step 1 Go to the page AAA.

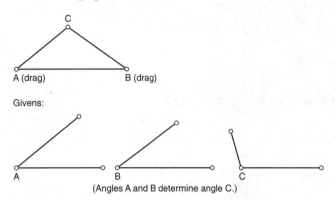

Step 2 Drag the points labeled *A* and *B* in the triangle.

Step 3 Change the measure of one or more of the given angles (the free angles below the triangles) and try the experiment again.

Investigate

1. Can you form two or more triangles with different sizes or shapes given the three angles?

2. If you are given two triangles such that the three angles in one triangle are congruent to the three angles in the other triangle (AAA), is that enough information to determine that the triangles are congruent?

3. Summarize your findings.

Lesson 4.8 • Special Triangle Conjectures

In this activity you will construct and investigate the properties of the angle bisector, altitude, and median of the vertex angle of isosceles triangles.

Investigation

Sketch

Step 1 In a new sketch, construct a circle with center *A* and control point *B*.

Step 2 Construct radius *AB*.

Step 3 Construct point *C* on the circle, and then construct radius *AC*.

Step 4 Construct $\overline{BC}$.

Step 5 Hide circle *AB*, leaving isosceles triangle *ABC*.

Step 6 Construct the bisector of ∠*CAB*, the vertex angle. To do this, select, in order, points *C*, *A*, and *B*, and choose **Construct | Angle Bisector.**

Step 7 Construct $\overline{AD}$, where *D* is the intersection of the angle bisector with the triangle.

Step 8 Hide the ray that forms the angle bisector.

Investigate

1. Segment *AD* is the angle bisector segment of the vertex angle of △*ABC*. Is there anything else special about it? To investigate, measure angles *ADB* and *ADC*. What do these measures indicate about $\overline{AD}$?

2. Measure *BD* and *DC*. What is special about point *D*?

3. Your answer to Question 2 demonstrates that $\overline{AD}$ is also what kind of special segment?

4. Combine your answers to Questions 1–3 to write a conjecture about three special segments in an isosceles triangle (Vertex Angle Bisector Conjecture).

EXPLORE MORE

1. Is the converse of your conjecture true? Construct and label an arbitrary △*ABC*. Construct the angle bisector, the altitude, and the median of one angle. Drag vertices until the three lines coincide. What kind of triangle is △*ABC* now? Investigate.

2. Construct an isosceles triangle *ABC*. Construct the angle bisector, the median, and the altitude of a nonvertex angle. Try to make these three lines concurrent. Make a conjecture based on your findings.

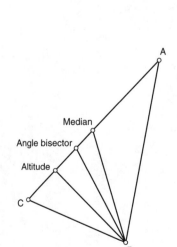

Lesson 5.1 • Polygon Sum Conjecture

You discovered that the angle measures of any triangle always sum to the same number. Do you think that the same will be true for other polygons?

Investigation: Is There a Polygon Sum Formula?

Sketch

Step 1 In a new sketch, construct a quadrilateral.

Step 2 Measure all four angles of the quadrilateral. Make sure that the vertex is the second point you select on each angle.

Step 3 Use the calculator to sum all the angle measures. Click on each measurement to enter it into the calculator.

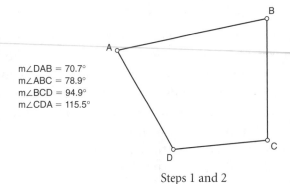

m∠DAB = 70.7°
m∠ABC = 78.9°
m∠BCD = 94.9°
m∠CDA = 115.5°

Steps 1 and 2

Investigate

1. Drag vertices of the quadrilateral and observe the angle sum. For now, just consider the angle sum in convex quadrilaterals. Record your observations as a conjecture (Quadrilateral Sum Conjecture).

Now you'll extend your conjecture about quadrilaterals to polygons with more than four sides. Before you get started, you need to decide a few things in your group.

2. There are many different types of polygons with more than four sides—pentagons, hexagons, octagons, and so on. Decide which convex polygon your group would like to investigate. Make sure that no other group is investigating the same polygon.

3. Let n represent the number of sides of your polygon. What is n for your polygon?

4. What is the name of your polygon, if it has one?

5. Before you explore the sum of the angles of your polygon on Sketchpad, predict what you will discover. Record your prediction and explain why you think it is reasonable.

6. Construct your convex polygon and calculate the sum of all its angles. Drag different vertices of your polygon and describe how well your sketch confirms your prediction from Question 5.

7. Compare your results with results from groups that investigated other polygons. After you study the different results, write a conjecture that generalizes the sum of the angles for any convex polygon with n sides (Polygon Sum Conjecture).

(continued)

EXPLORE MORE

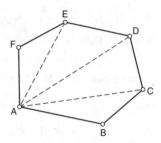

1. Construct a polygon with more than four sides. Use dashed segments to connect one of the vertices to every other vertex. (Because the vertex is already connected to its neighboring vertices, you don't need to construct these two segments again.) You have dissected your polygon into triangles. Use this sketch to explain why the Polygon Sum Conjecture follows directly from the Triangle Sum Conjecture.

2. Now you can explore the concave polygons you have ignored so far. Your book defines an angle's measure to be between 0° and 180°. Sketchpad will give angle measures up to and including 180°, but not greater. By that definition, there is no interior angle at a "caved-in" vertex of a concave polygon. If you consider these points to be vertices of interior angles with measures greater than 180°, does the Polygon Sum Conjecture still hold? Use a polygon like the one from Explore More 1 to investigate this question.

3. Calculate the measure of an angle of a *regular* octagon. Use this information to construct a regular octagon by repeatedly rotating a segment by this angle. Save or print your regular octagon.

Lesson 5.2 • Exterior Angles

Demonstration

If you extend each side of a convex polygon in one direction (either all clockwise or all counterclockwise), you create a *set of exterior angles*. Here you'll investigate the sum of the measures of one set of exterior angles in a polygon.

Sketch

Step 1 Open the sketch **Exterior Angles Demo.gsp.**

Step 2 Drag each vertex of the pentagon and observe how the exterior angle measures change.

Step 3 Press *Show Sum.*

Step 4 Drag each vertex again and observe the effect on the sum.

Step 5 Make sure the polygon is convex, then press *Shrink Polygon.* Observe the effects on the polygon and the angle measures.

Step 6 To repeat the experiment for another pentagon, press *Stretch Back Out,* drag one or more vertices to change the polygon, then shrink it again.

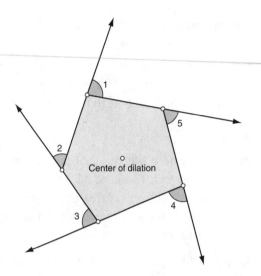

Step 7 To try the experiment for a quadrilateral, stretch the polygon back out, press *One Less Side,* then shrink the polygon.

Step 8 To try the experiment for a triangle, stretch the quadrilateral back out, press *Another Side Less,* then shrink the polygon.

Investigate

1. What is the sum of the measures of one set of exterior angles in any pentagon, quadrilateral, or triangle?

2. Do you think your answer to Question 1 can be generalized for any polygon? If so, explain why you think the sum of the measures of one set of exterior angles is what it is.

3. Explain what happens to exterior angles and their sum when the polygon is concave.

Lesson 5.2 • Exterior Angles of a Polygon

An exterior angle of a convex polygon is formed when you extend any side of the polygon. Exterior angles lie outside the polygon. In this investigation you'll discover the sum of the measures of a polygon's exterior angles. You will also discover a formula for finding the interior angle of any equiangular polygon.

Investigation 1: Is There an Exterior Angle Sum?

Each group should choose a different polygon for this investigation. The pictures here show the construction steps for a quadrilateral. The steps are essentially the same for any polygon, so don't let the pictures confuse you if you have picked one that has more than four sides.

Sketch

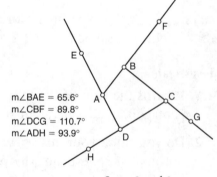

Step 1 In a new sketch, choose the **Ray** tool and construct a polygon and its exterior angles. Make sure your polygon is convex. (*Note:* This construction creates only one set of exterior angles. You would construct a different set if you went in the opposite direction with your rays.)

Step 2 Add a point to every ray on the part that extends beyond the polygon. These points are necessary for measuring the exterior angles.

Step 3 Measure all the exterior angles. Make sure you measure the correct angles! You should have as many measures as there are sides to your polygon.

Step 4 Calculate the sum of the exterior angles.

Step 1

$m\angle BAE = 65.6°$
$m\angle CBF = 89.8°$
$m\angle DCG = 110.7°$
$m\angle ADH = 93.9°$

Steps 2 and 3

Investigate

1. Drag vertices of your polygon to see if the sum changes, making sure your polygon remains convex. Record your observations.

2. Compare your results with other results in your class. After comparing the exterior angle sums of different polygons, write a conjecture (Exterior Angle Sum Conjecture).

Investigation 2: Equiangular Polygon Conjecture

Your knowledge about angles of polygons will help you construct regular polygons. Recall that a regular polygon is both equilateral and equiangular. For this investigation, it is more interesting to use polygons with many sides.

(continued)

Lesson 5.2 • Exterior Angles of a Polygon (continued)

Investigate

1. Pick a polygon with more than five sides. Assume your polygon is equiangular and figure out the measure of an interior angle. Record your results and explain your method.

Sketch

Step 1 Construct a segment.

Step 2 Double-click an endpoint of the segment to mark it as a center of rotation.

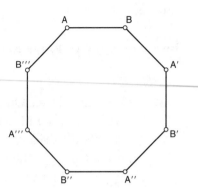

Step 3 Rotate the segment by the angle you found in Question 1. (To do this, select the segment *and its other endpoint* and choose **Transform | Rotate.** Then enter the appropriate angle measurement.)

Step 4 Figure out how to construct the rest of your regular polygon.

Investigate

2. Find a formula that will calculate the measure of an interior angle for any equiangular *n*-gon. It will help if you first compare the angle in your construction with angles in other polygons in your class. Write your formula in the form of a conjecture (Equiangular Polygon Conjecture).

3. Is your equiangular polygon also equilateral?

4. Describe an equiangular polygon that is not equilateral.

EXPLORE MORE

1. Repeat Step 1 of Investigation 1 to construct a polygon with a set of exterior angles, or use your sketch from that investigation if you still have it. Double-click any point to mark it as a center. Choose **Edit | Select All,** then use the **Dilate** tool to drag the selection toward the center point. (To get the **Dilate** tool, press and hold the **Arrow** tool button and choose the tool on the far right.) Write a paragraph to describe your observations. Use these questions to help you.

   a. As your polygon gets smaller and smaller, what happens to the exterior angles?

   b. What can you say about the angles as the polygon approaches a single point?

   c. How does this illustrate your Exterior Angle Sum Conjecture?

2. Construct a polygon that is equiangular but not equilateral.

Lesson 5.3 • Kite and Trapezoid Properties

You learned the definitions of different kinds of quadrilaterals in Chapter 2. Keep these definitions handy, because you may need to refer to them. In the next few lessons you will learn more about the properties of different quadrilaterals. In this activity you will discover properties of kites and trapezoids.

Investigation 1: What Are Some Properties of Kites?

Sketch

Step 1 Open the sketch **Quad Family.gsp.** Drag different vertices of the quadrilaterals and determine which quadrilateral is the kite. You will use this quadrilateral for the rest of this investigation, so drag it to another part of the screen and make it large. If you prefer, you can copy it and paste it into a new sketch.

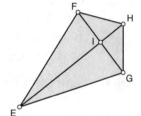

Step 2 Construct both diagonals of the kite.

Step 3 Construct the point of intersection of the diagonals.

Step 4 Measure all four angles of your kite.

Investigate

1. Drag vertices of the kite and observe the measures of the vertex angles and the nonvertex angles. Summarize your observations as the Kite Angles Conjecture.

2. Drag vertices of the kite and observe how the diagonals intersect. Measure an angle formed by the diagonals to check your observations.

3. The **vertex angles** of a kite are the angles formed by pairs of congruent sides. Decide which diagonal connects the vertex angles of the kite. Then observe how this diagonal divides the other diagonal. Drag vertices and measure distances to check your observations. (To measure a distance between points, select the two points and choose **Measure | Distance.**) Summarize your observations as the Kite Diagonal Bisector Conjecture.

4. The diagonals divide each angle of the kite into two new angles. Drag vertices of the kite and make observations about how each diagonal divides the vertex angles and the nonvertex angles. Measure some of the smaller angles to check your observations. Summarize your findings as the Kite Angle Bisector Conjecture.

(continued)

Discovering Geometry with The Geometer's Sketchpad
©2008 Key Curriculum Press

Lesson 5.3 • Kite and Trapezoid Properties (continued)

Investigation 2: What Are Some Properties of Trapezoids?

Sketch

Step 1 Look back at the sketch **Quad Family.gsp.** Drag
different vertices of the remaining quadrilaterals and
determine which quadrilaterals are trapezoids. In an
isosceles trapezoid, the two nonparallel sides are the
same length. Do not use the isosceles trapezoid until
the next investigation. Because you will use the ordinary
trapezoid for the rest of this investigation, drag it to
another part of the screen and make it large. If you
prefer, you can copy it and paste it into a new sketch.

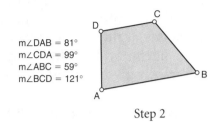

m∠DAB = 81°
m∠CDA = 99°
m∠ABC = 59°
m∠BCD = 121°

Step 2

Step 2 Measure all four angles of the trapezoid.

Investigate

1. The two parallel sides of the trapezoid are called *bases*. Find a pair of
consecutive angles that lie between the bases. There are two such pairs.
Rearrange your angle measurements to match up these consecutive
pairs. Drag vertices of the trapezoid and observe the angle pairs. Make
calculations to check your observations. Then summarize your
observations as the Trapezoid Consecutive Angles Conjecture.

Sketch

Step 3 Drag different parts of the remaining
quadrilaterals and find the isosceles trapezoid.

Step 4 Measure all four angles of the trapezoid.

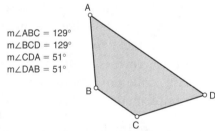

m∠ABC = 129°
m∠BCD = 129°
m∠CDA = 51°
m∠DAB = 51°

Investigate

2. Drag different vertices of the isosceles trapezoid and observe
the angle measures. Summarize your observations as the
Isosceles Trapezoid Conjecture.

3. Construct the diagonals of the isosceles trapezoid and measure
both of their lengths. Drag vertices of the trapezoid and make
observations about their lengths. Summarize your observations
as the Isosceles Trapezoid Diagonals Conjecture.

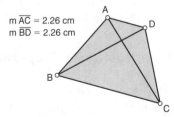

m $\overline{AC}$ = 2.26 cm
m $\overline{BD}$ = 2.26 cm

EXPLORE MORE

For each of the constructions in Questions 1–3, drag vertices to make sure
your construction has enough constraints to keep the polygon you want,
but not too many to represent some versions of the polygon. You might
want to make **Custom** tools of these to use in the future.

1. Construct a kite.

2. Construct a trapezoid.

3. Construct an isosceles trapezoid.

4. Concave kites are called *darts*. Do the kite conjectures hold for darts?

Lesson 5.4 • Properties of Midsegments

As you learned in Chapter 3, when you connect the midpoints of two sides of a triangle, you create a **midsegment.** The segment connecting the midpoints of the two nonparallel sides of a trapezoid is also called a midsegment. In this activity you will construct midsegments of triangles and trapezoids and investigate their properties.

Investigation 1: Triangle Midsegment Properties

Sketch

Step 1 In a new sketch, construct a triangle.

Step 2 Construct the midpoint of each side. (To do this, select each side and choose **Midpoints** from the Construct menu.)

Step 3 Construct all three midsegments by connecting the midpoints.

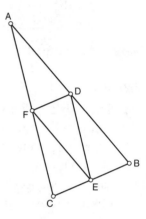

Investigate

1. Drag vertices of your original triangle and observe the four small triangles. How do they compare? Make appropriate measurements to check your observations. Then summarize your observations about the four triangles as the Three Midsegments Conjecture.

2. Select a midsegment and change its line width to **Thick** using the Display menu. Now find the side of the original triangle that the midsegment is not connected to and make that side thick as well. Before making any measurements, drag a vertex of your original triangle and make predictions about relationships between the midsegment and this third side.

   m $\overline{CA}$ = 3.58 cm
   m $\overline{ED}$ = 1.79 cm
   Slope $\overline{CA}$ = −0.31
   Slope $\overline{ED}$ = −0.31

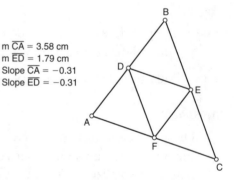

3. Measure the length and slope of both thick segments. Drag vertices of the original triangle and compare the slopes and lengths of these segments. Summarize your observations as the Triangle Midsegment Conjecture.

Investigation 2: Trapezoid Midsegment Properties

Sketch

Step 1 If you made a tool to construct trapezoids in the previous lesson, open it. Otherwise, open the sketch **Quad Family.gsp.** Drag different parts of the quadrilaterals and determine which one is the trapezoid. Use the ordinary trapezoid, *not* the isosceles trapezoid. You will use this quadrilateral for the rest of this investigation, so drag it to another part of the screen and make it large. If you prefer, you can copy it and paste it into a new sketch.

(continued)

Discovering Geometry with The Geometer's Sketchpad
©2008 Key Curriculum Press

Lesson 5.4 • Properties of Midsegments (continued)

Step 2 The **midsegment** of a trapezoid is the segment connecting the midpoints of the nonparallel sides. Construct the midsegment of your trapezoid.

Step 3 Measure the slopes of the midsegment and the parallel sides.

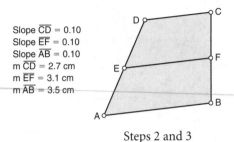

Slope $\overline{CD}$ = 0.10
Slope $\overline{EF}$ = 0.10
Slope $\overline{AB}$ = 0.10
m $\overline{CD}$ = 2.7 cm
m $\overline{EF}$ = 3.1 cm
m $\overline{AB}$ = 3.5 cm

Steps 2 and 3

Investigate

1. Drag vertices of your trapezoid and write a conjecture based on your observations.

2. Now measure the lengths of the midsegment and the parallel sides. Make a prediction about how the length of the midsegment compares with the lengths of the parallel sides. Check your prediction using Sketchpad's calculator. (You may need to use parentheses.) Summarize your observations as a second conjecture about the midsegment of a trapezoid.

3. Now combine your results from your last two conjectures to make a single conjecture about the midsegment of a trapezoid (Trapezoid Midsegment Conjecture).

Lesson 5.5 • Properties of Parallelograms

A parallelogram is a quadrilateral whose opposite sides are parallel. In this activity you will investigate properties of parallelograms.

Investigation: Four Parallelogram Properties

Sketch

First, you will construct a parallelogram using the definition.

Step 1 Construct segment *AB* and point *C* above the segment.

Step 2 Construct a line through *C* parallel to segment *AB*. (Select the segment and the point and choose **Construct | Parallel Line.**)

Step 3 Construct segment *AC*.

Step 4 Construct a line through *B* parallel to segment *AC*.

Step 5 Construct the point of intersection of the two lines. Label the point *D*.

Step 6 Hide both lines, and finish your parallelogram by constructing the missing segments.

Step 7 Drag different vertices of your parallelogram to check that you constructed it properly.

Step 8 Measure all four angles of your parallelogram.

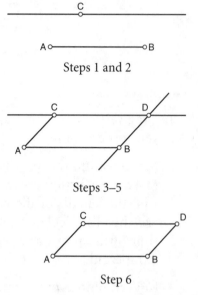

Steps 1 and 2

Steps 3–5

Step 6

Investigate

1. Drag vertices to observe these angle measures, then write the Parallelogram Opposite Angles Conjecture.

2. Choose **Measure | Calculate** to add the measures of pairs of consecutive angles in your parallelogram. Drag vertices to observe these angle sums, then write the Parallelogram Consecutive Angles Conjecture.

3. Measure the lengths of all four sides of your parallelogram. Drag vertices to observe these lengths, then write the Parallelogram Opposite Sides Conjecture.

4. Construct the diagonals of your parallelogram and their point of intersection. Label this point *E*. Measure *AE*, *ED*, *CE*, and *EB*. Drag vertices to observe these lengths, then write the Parallelogram Diagonals Conjecture.

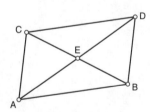

EXPLORE MORE

Find other ways to construct a parallelogram.

Using Your Algebra Skills 5 • Equations of Lines   Demonstration

In this demonstration you'll look for relationships between the equation of a line and its slope and *y*-intercept.

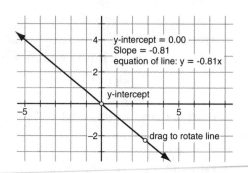

Sketch

Step 1 Open the sketch **Slope Intercept Demo.gsp.**

Step 2 Press the *Translate* and *Rotate* buttons and observe their effects on the line and on the measurements and equation.

Step 3 Drag the points *y-intercept* and *drag to rotate line*, and observe what changes in the sketch. Do not press *Make Vertical* or *Reset* until you've answered the questions.

Investigate

1. Dragging the point *y-intercept* has the same effect as what action button?

2. What measurement changes when you press *Translate*?

3. What part of the equation changes when you press *Translate*?

4. Dragging the point *drag to rotate line* has the same effect as what button?

5. What measurement changes when you press *Rotate*?

6. What part of the equation changes when you press *Rotate*?

7. If a line has slope *m* and *y*-intercept *b*, what is the equation of the line? (This is called the **slope-intercept form** of the equation.)

8. Make the line horizontal. What is its slope?

9. What is the equation of a horizontal line in slope-intercept form?

Sketch

Step 4 Press *Make Vertical*, and observe its effects. Do not press *Reset* until you've answered the following questions.

Step 5 Press *Translate Vertical Line*, or drag the point labeled *drag to translate line*.

Investigate

10. What is the equation of the line when it coincides with the *y*-axis?

11. What is the slope of a vertical line?

12. Which measurement disappears when the line becomes vertical? Why?

13. What is the equation of a vertical line that has *x*-intercept *c*?

14. Explain why the variable *y* doesn't appear in the equation of a vertical line.

Using Your Algebra Skills 5 • Writing Linear Equations

There are many ways of describing a line. A line is a straight path that extends forever. A line is also a collection of points that follow a certain rule or equation. A **linear equation** is an equation whose graph is a straight line. In this activity you will investigate linear equations.

Investigation: Equations of Lines

Sketch

Step 1 In a new sketch, construct a point anywhere and label it *Target*.

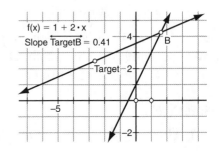

Step 2 Choose **Graph | Plot New Function,** and enter $1 + 2x$. A grid, a line, and an equation for the line will appear.

Step 3 Construct a point on the function plot.

Step 4 Construct a line through that point and point *Target.*

Step 5 Measure the slope of the line.

Investigate

1. Double-click on the line's equation and change the numbers (originally 1 and 2) to get the line to pass through point *Target.*

2. Repeat this process as many times as needed until you succeed. How do the function plot and the line compare?

3. In your algebra course, you may have learned one of these forms of a linear equation.

   Slope-intercept form: $y = mx + b$

   Intercept form: $y = a + bx$

   What do the numbers m and b (or a and b) represent on your graph?

4. Next you will create an action button that allows you to hide the line. To do this, select the line and choose **Edit | Action Button | Hide/Show.** A button will appear on your screen.

5. Press the button to hide your function plot. Now change the numbers in the equation of the function plot, as you did before. Drag the *Target* point until you think the line showing satisfies that new equation. Finally, press *Show Function Plot* to test your prediction. Do this a few times. How good were your predictions?

EXPLORE MORE

Suppose a pair of parallel lines have *y*-intercepts that are 2 units apart. Does this mean that the lines are 2 units apart from each other? Construct such a pair of lines to investigate this question. Explain how the distance between these parallel lines depends on their slopes.

Lesson 5.6 • Properties of Special Parallelograms

You have discovered some properties that hold true for any parallelogram. Now you will discover some properties that are true only for special types of parallelograms.

Investigation 1: Do Rhombus Diagonals Have Special Properties?

A **rhombus** is a parallelogram with four congruent sides.

Sketch

Step 1 Open the sketch **Quad Family.gsp.** Drag different vertices of the quadrilaterals and determine which quadrilateral is always a rhombus (but is not always a square). You will use this quadrilateral for the rest of this investigation, so drag it to another part of the screen and make it large. If you prefer, you can copy it and paste it into a new sketch.

Step 2 Construct the diagonals of the rhombus.

Step 3 Construct the point of intersection of the diagonals.

Investigate

1. Drag the vertices of the rhombus and observe the diagonals. Find two properties that describe how the diagonals intersect. Make measurements to verify your observations. Then summarize your findings as the Rhombus Diagonals Conjecture.

2. Now drag different vertices and observe how each diagonal intersects the angles of the rhombus. Make some angle measurements to verify your observations. Then summarize your findings as the Rhombus Angles Conjecture.

Investigation 2: Do Rectangle Diagonals Have Special Properties?

A rectangle is an equiangular parallelogram.

Sketch

Step 1 Look back at the sketch **Quad Family.gsp.** Drag different vertices of the quadrilaterals and determine which quadrilateral is always a rectangle (but is not always a square). You will use this quadrilateral for the rest of this investigation, so drag it to another part of the screen and make it large. If you prefer, you can copy it and paste it into a new sketch.

Step 2 Measure at least two of the angles of the rectangle. (You probably won't need to measure the others.)

(continued)

Investigate

1. Drag vertices of the rectangle and write a conjecture about the measure of its angles.

2. Construct both diagonals of the rectangle. Drag vertices of the rectangle and observe the diagonals. Make measurements to verify your observations. Then write a conjecture about the diagonals of a rectangle (Rectangle Diagonals Conjecture).

Sketch

Step 3 Go back to the sketch **Quad Family.gsp.** Drag different vertices of the quadrilaterals and determine which quadrilateral is always a square.

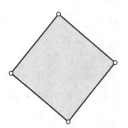

Investigate

3. Test the conjectures you made for rhombuses and rectangles on the square. Which of them hold for the square?

4. You may have noticed that you haven't been given a definition of a square. Instead, you will write your own.

   a. First write a definition of a square that uses the word *rhombus.*

   b. Now write a definition of a square that uses the word *rectangle.*

5. Using what you know about the diagonals of parallelograms, rectangles, and rhombuses, write a conjecture about the diagonals of a square (Square Diagonals Conjecture).

Explore more

In Questions 1–3, construct each parallelogram. Drag vertices to make sure your construction has enough constraints to keep the polygon you want, but not too many to represent some versions of the polygon.

1. Construct a rhombus.

2. Construct a rectangle.

3. Construct a square.

4. Construct a parallelogram.

   a. Bisect a pair of opposite angles of the parallelogram. Make a conjecture about these angle bisectors. Explain why your conjecture is true.

   b. Follow the procedure in part a for a pair of consecutive angles.

Lesson 5.7 • Variations on the Crane

Extension

You probably have seen a Japanese origami crane; maybe you have folded one yourself. In this activity you'll fold a traditional origami crane, then you'll use The Geometer's Sketchpad to explore other shapes you can fold into a crane. You will need a square piece of paper. You can cut a rectangular piece of plain paper into a square, or use patty paper or origami paper.

Investigation: Square Cranes

FOLDING A CRANE

Step 1   Fold a square piece of paper in half diagonally to make crease *AC*, then in half diagonally again to make crease *DE*.

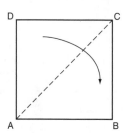
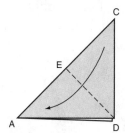

Step 2   Lift the top triangle, △*CED*, and slide your finger in along the center crease to open the triangle up. Match point *C* to point *D*, and crease to make square *EGFC*.

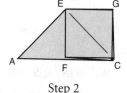

Step 3   Turn the figure over and repeat Step 2 on the other side, matching point *A* to point *B* to make square *EHAJ*. How does this square compare to the original square?

Step 2

Step 4   Orient the figure so that the opening, point *A*, is pointing down. Fold and crease the angle bisectors of ∠*JAE* and ∠*HAE*. Fold and crease △*EKL*. Unfold the top triangle and the side triangles.

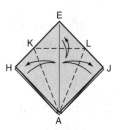

Step 5   Using $\overline{KL}$ as the diagonal, lift the top layer all the way up and flatten down the sides to make *AKDL*. What kind of quadrilateral is this? How do you know?

Step 4

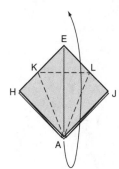
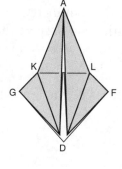

Step 6   Turn the figure over and repeat Steps 4 and 5 on the other side to make *CKDL*. Orient the figure so point *D/B* is pointing down.

(continued)

Step 7   Fold the outside part of each leg into the center and crease.

Step 8   Turn the figure over and repeat Step 7 on the other side.

Step 9   Open the right side and flatten it. Lift the right leg up as far as it will go. This will be either the head or the tail. Choose an angle that looks nice and flatten it down, reversing the folds along the crease.

Step 10 Repeat Step 9 on the left side.

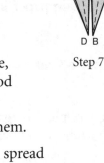

Step 7   Step 9

Step 11 Decide which side you want to be the head. On that side, open the tip and reverse-fold it down as far as looks good to you.

Step 12 Fold the wings down as far as they will go, and crease them.

Step 13 Gently pull the wings out to each side. The back should spread out and open up. If you're using thin paper, you can also blow sharply into the hole in the center bottom.

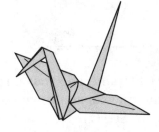

Step 11   Steps 12–13

Investigate: Symmetries of the Crane

Soon you'll use Sketchpad to make a pattern for a nonsquare crane. But first, let's look at which relationships are important for the pattern.

1. Very carefully, unfold your crane and flatten it. On a clean sheet of paper, use your geometry tools to construct the pattern of the folds you made in Steps 1–4. These are the basic folds of the crane. How many lines of symmetry does the pattern have? Label them on your drawing.

2. Now look at your unfolded crane. How many lines of symmetry does the actual crane have? Explain. Which line(s) are these on your drawing?

3. Any shape you use to fold a crane should have this symmetry. Look at your drawing. What are some other characteristics you suspect the nonsquare pattern might need to have in order to be able to fold it into a crane?

Now you'll use what you learned about the symmetries of the crane to construct a new crane pattern in Sketchpad.

SKETCH

Step 14 In a new sketch, construct triangle *ABC*.

Step 15 Double-click $\overline{AC}$ to mark it as a mirror. Select $\overline{AB}$, $\overline{BC}$, and point *B*, and choose **Transform | Reflect.** What is true about *ABCB′*?

(continued)

Discovering Geometry with The Geometer's Sketchpad
©2008 Key Curriculum Press

Lesson 5.7 • Variations on the Crane (continued)

Step 16 Construct the bisector of ∠B by selecting points A, B, and C, in that order, and choosing **Construct | Angle Bisector.** Construct the bisector of ∠B′ in the same way. These bisectors correspond to which folds in your drawing?

Step 17 Click on the intersection of the angle bisectors to construct it. Construct $\overline{DB}$ and $\overline{DB'}$ and hide the angle-bisector rays. Now construct the angle bisectors of all the angles around the edge of the figure. Remember to select three points for each angle, with the vertex as the second selection.

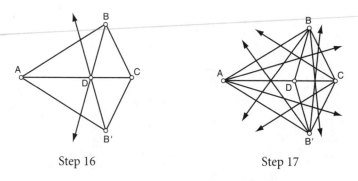

Step 16   Step 17

Step 18 Drag your construction to look more like a square. Using your hand drawing as a guide, construct the intersections of the angle bisectors. Construct segments on the angle bisectors and hide the rays.

Step 19 Construct a line through points D and E. Construct the intersection of the line with $\overline{BC}$, and then construct $\overline{DI}$. Hide the line. Follow the same steps for the other three angle-bisector intersections. Which folds are these segments in your drawing?

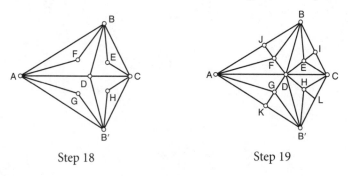

Step 18   Step 19

Investigate

4. Construct $\overline{EF}$, $\overline{FG}$, $\overline{GH}$, and $\overline{HE}$. You now have a pattern you can use to construct a crane out of any quadrilateral with bilateral symmetry. How do the characteristics of this pattern compare to your predictions in Question 3?

5. Drag the pattern around. Using this pattern, what shapes can you fold into a crane?

Step 20 Choose a shape you like, print it out, and fold your crane.

Lesson 6.1 • Tangents to Circles   Demonstration

In this demonstration you will investigate some important properties of tangents to circles.

Investigation 1: Secant Segments Becoming Tangents

A **secant** is a line, ray or segment that intersects a circle in two points. Here you will use secant segments to explore properties of tangent segments.

Sketch

Step 1   Open the sketch **Tangents to Circles Demo.gsp.**

Step 2   Drag points B and C until both secant rays are tangent to the circle.

Investigate

1. How are the lengths of the tangent segments $\overline{BD}$ and $\overline{CD}$ related? Drag D to another place outside the circle, then reposition B and C to get tangent rays again. Does the relationship still hold? Summarize your findings in a conjecture (Tangent Segments Conjecture).

2. How are the tangent rays related to the radii at the points of tangency? Does this relationship hold for other positions of D? Summarize your findings in a conjecture (Tangent Conjecture).

3. Write down the converse of the Tangent Conjecture from Question 2. How might you check to see if it is valid?

Investigation 2: Converse of the Tangent Conjecture

Sketch

Step 3   Go to Page 2 in the same sketch.

Step 4   Press *Show Perpendicular Line* to reveal a line that was constructed through point B perpendicular to radius $\overline{AB}$.

Investigate

4. Drag point B around the circle. How many times does the perpendicular line intersect the circle? Does this ever change?

5. How does your answer to Question 4 relate to the converse of the Tangent Conjecture?

6. How can you use the converse of the Tangent conjecture to construct a tangent to a circle?

Lesson 6.1 • Tangent Properties

Investigation 1: Going Off on a Tangent

In this investigation you'll discover a relationship between a tangent line and the radius drawn to the point of tangency.

Sketch

Step 1   In a new sketch, construct circle *AB* and radius $\overline{AB}$.

Step 2   Construct point *C* on the circle, and construct line *BC*.

Step 3   Measure ∠*CBA*. (*Remember,* to measure an angle, make sure the vertex is the second point you select.)

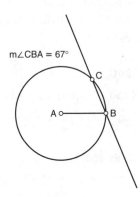

Investigate

1. Drag point *C* toward point *B* and watch the angle measurement change. When point *C* appears to coincide with point *B*, the line will be approximately tangent. What's the measure of ∠*CBA*? Write a conjecture about a tangent and the radius drawn to the point of tangency (Tangent Conjecture).

Investigation 2: Tangent Segments

Investigation 1 may have given you an idea of how to construct a tangent to a circle. In this investigation you'll construct two tangents and investigate a relationship between the distances from the points of tangency to the point where the tangents intersect.

Sketch

Step 1   In a new sketch, construct circle *AB* and radius $\overline{AB}$.

Step 2   To construct a tangent, select point *B* and $\overline{AB}$ and choose **Construct | Perpendicular Line.**

Step 3   Construct $\overline{AC}$, where point *C* is a point on the circle.

Step 4   Construct a tangent through point *C*.

Step 5   Construct point *D* where these tangent lines intersect.

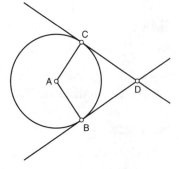

Investigate

1. The two tangent lines intersect at a point outside the circle to form tangent segments (unless the lines are parallel). Measure *BD* and *CD*. (Select the points and choose **Measure | Distance.**) Drag point *C* and observe the measurements. Write a conjecture about tangent segments (Tangent Segments Conjecture).

Lesson 6.2 • Chord Properties

In this lesson you will discover some properties of chords, arcs, and central angles.

Investigation 1: Chords and Their Central Angles

Sketch

Step 1   In a new sketch, construct circle *AB*.

Step 2   Construct point *C* on the circle, and then construct the chord $\overline{BC}$.

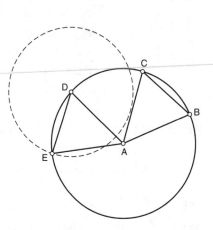

Step 3   Construct point *D* on the circle.

Step 4   Select $\overline{BC}$ and point *D*, and choose **Construct | Circle By Center+Radius.**

Step 5   Construct $\overline{DE}$ so that point *E* is a point of intersection of this new circle and circle *AB*.

Step 6   Hide the circle centered at point *D*.

Step 7   Construct segments *AB*, *AC*, *AD*, and *AE*.

Investigate

1. Drag different parts of your figure to confirm that the chords you constructed stay congruent. Measure central angles *CAB* and *DAE*. (*Remember*, to measure an angle, make sure the vertex is the second point you select.) Write a conjecture about congruent chords in a circle and the central angles they determine (Chord Central Angles Conjecture).

2. The measure of a minor arc is defined as the measure of its central angle. Select point *B*, point *C*, and the circle, and choose **Measure | Arc Angle** to confirm this. Measure the arc intercepted by the other chord. What can you conclude about congruent chords in a circle and the arcs they intercept? Write a conjecture (Chord Arcs Conjecture).

Investigation 2: Chords and the Center of the Circle

Sketch

Step 1   In your sketch from Investigation 1, hide the radius segments.

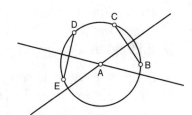

Step 2   Select chord *BC* and point *A*, and choose **Construct | Perpendicular Line.**

Step 3   Repeat Step 2 with chord *DE* and point *A*.

(continued)

Investigate

1. Drag point *C* and observe the relationship between the chord and the line perpendicular to it from the center of the circle. At what special point does the perpendicular line intersect the chord? Write a conjecture (Perpendicular to a Chord Conjecture).

2. Measure the distance from point *A* to $\overline{BC}$ and the distance from point *A* to $\overline{DE}$. (Select a point and a segment, and choose **Measure | Distance.**) Drag parts of your sketch and observe these distances for different pairs of congruent chords. Write a conjecture about congruent chords in a circle and their distances from the circle's center (Chord Distance to Center Conjecture).

Investigation 3: Perpendicular Bisector of a Chord

Now you'll investigate the converse of the conjecture you made in Question 1 of the last investigation.

Sketch

Step 1 In a new sketch, construct circle *AB*.

Step 2 Construct chord *BC*.

Step 3 Construct the midpoint *D* of $\overline{BC}$.

Step 4 Construct a line through point *D*, perpendicular to $\overline{BC}$.

Investigate

1. What do you notice about the perpendicular bisector of a chord? Drag parts of your sketch to confirm that this is always true, then write a conjecture (Perpendicular Bisector of a Chord Conjecture).

2. Hide the center of your circle. Now perform a construction to locate the center. Explain how you did it. (Choosing **Show All Hidden** is cheating!)

EXPLORE MORE

1. Use congruent triangles to explain why the Chord Central Angles Conjecture is true.

2. Drag point *C* to make $\overline{BC}$ longer without changing the size of the circle. Does the chord get closer to or farther from the center of the circle? Investigate this question. Describe what you did and state your findings as a conjecture.

3. Suppose a chord in one circle is congruent to a chord in a second circle, but the second circle has a greater radius than the first circle. Do the two chords determine congruent central angles? If not, which central angle has the greater measure? Investigate these questions. Describe what you did and state your findings as a conjecture.

Lesson 6.2 • Intersecting Tangents Conjecture   Demonstration

In this demonstration you will discover a relationship between the measure of an angle formed by two tangents and the measure of the intercepted arc.

Sketch

Step 1   Open the sketch **Intersecting Tangents Demo.gsp.**

Step 2   Drag points *A*, *B*, and *circle radius* to see which angle measures change.

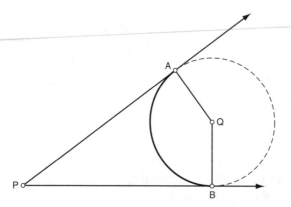

Investigate

1. What does the Tangent Conjecture say about rays *PA* and *PB*, and radii *QA* and *QB*? Move points *A* and *B*, and change the size of the circle's radius to confirm that the conjecture is true.

2. Move points *A*, *B*, and *circle radius* until $m\angle AQB = 160°$. What is $m\angle APB$?

3. Move points *A*, *B*, and *circle radius* until $m\widehat{AB} = 110°$. What is $m\angle APB$?

4. Continue to move points *A* and *B*, and observe the measures of the angles and arcs shown. Summarize your findings in a conjecture (Intersecting Tangents Conjecture).

5. Press *Show Quadrilateral.* Use the Quadrilateral Sum Conjecture, the Tangent Conjecture, and the definition of arc measure to explain why the Intersecting Tangents Conjecture is true.

Lesson 6.3 • Arcs and Angles

Investigation 1: Inscribed Angle Properties

In this investigation you'll discover a relationship between an inscribed angle and the arc it intercepts.

Sketch

Step 1 In a new sketch, construct circle *AB*.

Step 2 Construct $\overline{BC}$, where point *C* is a point on the circle.

Step 3 Construct $\overline{CD}$, where point *D* is another point on the circle.

Step 4 Measure ∠*DCB*.

Step 5 Select, in order, point *B*, point *D*, and the circle, and choose **Construct | Arc On Circle.** Change its line width to thick.

Step 6 Select the arc and choose **Measure | Arc Angle.**

m∠DCB = 50.38°
arc angle A = 100.77°

Investigate

1. Drag point *D* (but not past points *C* or *B*) and look for a relationship between the arc measure (called Arc Angle in Sketchpad) and the measure of the inscribed angle. Make a conjecture (Inscribed Angle Conjecture).

2. Drag point *C*. As long as you don't drag it past points *B* and *D*, the measurements don't change. Is your computer broken? Well, dragging point *C* doesn't do anything to the arc. What does that mean for all the inscribed angles that intercept that arc? If you're not sure, construct and measure another inscribed angle that intercepts $\overline{BD}$. Write a conjecture about inscribed angles that intercept the same arc (Inscribed Angles Intercepting Arcs Conjecture).

3. Construct segment *DB* and change its line width to dashed. Drag point *D* until $\overline{DB}$ passes through the circle's center. What is the measure of ∠*DCB*? Now drag point *C* to see if *m*∠*DCB* changes. Write a conjecture about angles inscribed in a semicircle (Angles Inscribed in a Semicircle Conjecture).

Investigation 2: Cyclic Quadrilaterals

Now you'll apply your previous discoveries to the angles of a quadrilateral inscribed in a circle, which is called a **cyclic quadrilateral.**

Sketch

Step 1 In a new sketch, construct circle *AB*.

Step 2 Use the **Segment** tool to construct quadrilateral *BCDE*, where points *C*, *D*, and *E* are also points on the circle.

Step 3 Measure the four angles of the quadrilateral.

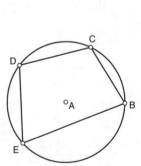

(continued)

Lesson 6.3 • Arcs and Angles (continued)

Investigate

1. Look for relationships between pairs of angles in the quadrilateral. Use the calculator to check any relationships you discover, then write a conjecture (Cyclic Quadrilateral Conjecture).

2. Explain why the Cyclic Quadrilateral Conjecture is true. (What kinds of angles did you measure? What is the sum of the arc measures of the two arcs intercepted by opposite angles in the quadrilateral?)

Investigation 3: Arcs by Parallel Lines

Now you'll discover a relationship between arcs formed when parallel lines intersect a circle.

Sketch

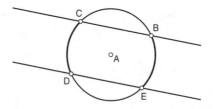

Step 1 In a new sketch, construct circle *AB*.

Step 2 Construct $\overleftrightarrow{BC}$, where point *C* is a point on the circle. (Drag points *B* and *C* to make sure the line is attached correctly.)

Step 3 Construct point *D* on the circle.

Step 4 Construct a line through point *D* parallel to $\overleftrightarrow{BC}$.

Step 5 Construct point *E* where the new line intersects the circle.

Step 6 Select, in order, point *E*, point *B*, and the circle. Choose **Construct | Arc On Circle.** Change the line width of this arc to thick.

Step 7 Construct $\overparen{CD}$ the same way. Make sure you select your points in counterclockwise order.

Investigate

1. Select each arc and measure its arc angle. Drag point *C* and observe the arcs and their measurements. Make a conjecture about the arcs intercepted by parallel lines (Parallel Lines Intercepted Arcs Conjecture).

EXPLORE MORE

Given a circle and a point outside the circle, find a method for constructing the two tangents from that point. Describe how you made your construction. (*Hint:* Start by constructing a segment from the point to the circle's center. Then construct the midpoint of that segment. You're on your own from here.)

Lesson 6.4 • Tangent-Chord Conjecture

In this demonstration you will discover a relationship between the measure of the angle, $\angle TNU$, at the intersection of the chord and tangent of a circle and the measures of the intercepted arcs, TN.

Sketch

Step 1 Open the sketch **Tangent Chord Demo.gsp.**

Step 2 Drag points A and B to see how the angle and arc measures change. See whether you can find a relationship between $m\angle ABC$ and $m\overarc{AB}$.

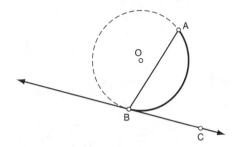

Investigate

1. Make a conjecture about the relationship between $m\angle ABC$ and $m\overarc{AB}$ (Tangent-Chord Conjecture).

2. Press *Show Radii*. What type of triangle is $\triangle OBA$? Why?

3. Use your answer to Question 2, along with the Triangle Sum Conjecture, to write an equation relating $m\overarc{AB}$ and $m\angle OBA$.

4. Use the Tangent Conjecture to write an equation relating $m\angle ABC$ and $m\angle OBA$.

5. Use the equations you wrote in Questions 3 and 4 to prove the Tangent-Chord Conjecture.

Lesson 6.5 • Circumference and Diameter   **Demonstration**

If you make a circle bigger, you increase both the distance across it (its diameter) and the distance around it (its circumference). The ratio of the circumference to the diameter is the same for any circle. In this demonstration you'll investigate this ratio.

Sketch

Step 1 Open the sketch **Circumference Demo.gsp.**

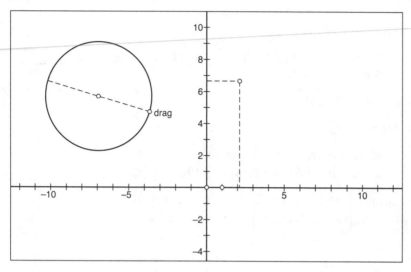

Step 2 Change the diameter of the circle in any of three ways: (1) drag point *drag;* (2) press the *1, 2,* or *3* button; or (3) press the *Animate* button.

Step 3 Observe how changing the size of the circle affects the point on the plot. Experiment with the sketch to answer the following questions, but don't press *Show Equation* until you've tried answering the questions.

Investigate

1. What does the *x*-coordinate of the point on the plot represent?

2. What does the *y*-coordinate of the point on the plot represent?

3. The ratio of the circumference of the circle to its diameter is a constant, represented by the Greek letter π (pi). What is the value of π to the nearest thousandth?

4. What is the slope of the line? What does the slope represent?

5. Write the equation of the line in terms of *x* and *y*. Press *Show Equation* to check your answer.

6. Rewrite the equation for the line in terms of *C, d,* and π.

Lesson 6.5 • The Circumference/Diameter Ratio

In this lesson you'll discover a relationship between a circle's circumference and its diameter. Even if that relationship is familiar to you, the investigation may demonstrate it in a different way.

Investigation: A Taste of Pi

Sketch

Step 1 In a new sketch, construct $\overline{AB}$.

Step 2 Construct point C, the midpoint of $\overline{AB}$.

Step 3 Construct circle CB. Be sure the cursor is positioned directly on point B when you release the mouse button.

Step 4 Measure the circumference of the circle.

Step 5 Measure AB (the diameter of the circle).

Step 6 Make the circle small. Select, in order, the diameter measurement and the circumference measurement. Choose **Graph | Plot As (x, y)**.

Step 7 Change the color of the plotted point so you can distinguish it from other points on the plot, and choose **Display | Trace Plotted Point.**

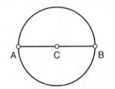

Investigate

1. Drag A or B to change your circle, and watch the plotted point. How does this demonstrate that the circumference/diameter ratio is the same for all circles?

2. Construct a line that covers the trace, and measure its slope.

3. Long ago, mathematicians named the circumference/diameter ratio with the Greek letter π (pi). Carefully write a conjecture relating the circumference and diameter of a circle and the number π. Then rewrite the conjecture using the radius of the circle (Circumference Conjecture).

Lesson 6.5 • Intersecting Chords Conjecture   Demonstration

In this demonstration you will discover a relationship between the measure of the angles formed by two chords in a circle and the measures of the intercepted arcs.

Sketch

Step 1   Open the sketch **Intersecting Chords Demo.gsp.**

Step 2   Drag points *A*, *L*, *N*, and *G* to see how the angle and arc measures change. Make sure chords always intersect.

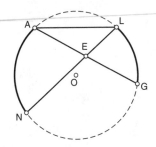

Investigate

1. What relationships do you notice between $m\angle AEN$ (or $m\angle LEG$) and the measures of $\overset{\frown}{AN}$ and $\overset{\frown}{LG}$? Start by comparing the relative sizes of the three values.

2. Press *Show Calculation*. What is the mathematical name for the calculation shown? Make a conjecture about the angle of two intersecting chords (Intersecting Chords Conjecture).

3. Press *Show Inscribed Angles*. Use the Inscribed Angles Conjecture to express *n* and *s* in terms of $\overset{\frown}{AN}$ and $\overset{\frown}{LG}$.

4. Use the Triangle Exterior Angle Conjecture to express $m\angle AEN$ in terms of *n* and *s*.

5. Put your answers from Questions 3 and 4 together to prove the Intersecting Chords Conjecture.

Lesson 6.6 • Intersecting Secants Conjecture   Demonstration

In this demonstration you will discover a relationship between the measure
of the angle formed by two intersecting secants of a circle and the
measures of the intercepted arcs.

Sketch

Step 1   Open the sketch **Intersecting Secants Demo.gsp.**

Step 2   Drag points *S*, *N*, and *C* to see how the angle and arc measures
change. Make sure there are always two secants.

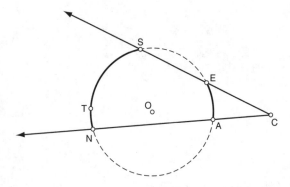

Investigate

1. Drag the points, making sure there are two secants and the secants
   intersect at a point outside the circle. Observe the measures of the two
   arcs and the measure of the angle at the intersection *C*.

2. Press *Show Difference.* What is the relationship between $m\angle SCN$ and
   $m\widehat{STN} - m\widehat{AE}$? Use your observations to make a conjecture
   (Intersecting Secants Conjecture).

3. Press *Show Chord.* Use the Inscribed Angle Conjecture to express the
   measures *a* and *b* in terms of $m\widehat{STN}$ and $m\widehat{AE}$.

4. Use the Triangle Exterior Angle Conjecture and your answer to
   Question 3 to prove the Intersecting Secants Conjecture.

Lesson 6.7 • Tangent-Secant Conjecture   **Demonstration**

In this demonstration you will discover a relationship between the measure of the angle at the intersection of a secant and a tangent of a circle and the measures of the intercepted arcs.

Sketch

Step 1 Open the sketch **Tangent Secant Demo.gsp.**

Step 2 Drag points *P*, *A*, and *B* to see how the angle and arc measures change.

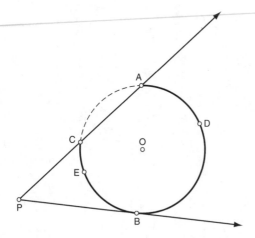

Investigate

1. Drag the points and observe the measures of the two arcs, $\overarc{CEB}$ and $\overarc{BDA}$.

2. Press *Show Difference*. What is the relationship between $m\angle APB$ and the difference shown? Use your observations to make a conjecture (Tangent-Secant Conjecture).

3. Press *Show Chord*. Use the Inscribed Angle Conjecture and the Tangent-Chord Conjecture to express the measures *a* and *b* in terms of $m\overarc{CEB}$ and $m\overarc{BDA}$.

4. Use the Triangle Exterior Angles Conjecture and your answer to Question 3 to prove the Tangent-Secant Conjecture.

Lesson 7.1 • Transformations and Symmetry

A **transformation** is a way of moving or changing an object. There are three types of basic transformations that preserve the size and shape of the object. These three—**reflections, rotations,** and **translations**—are called **isometries.** Isometries are also called **rigid transformations** because they move, turn, or reflect an object, but never bend or distort it. In this activity, you'll experiment with basic isometries by transforming the letter **F.**

Investigation: Translate, Rotate, and Reflect

Sketch

Step 1 In a new sketch, construct the letter **F** and its interior. (One way to do this is to use the **Point** tool with the Shift key to construct consecutive vertices of the letter, then choose **Measure | Polygon Interior.**)

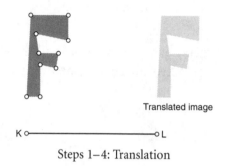

Translated image

Step 2 In order to translate a shape, you need to indicate a direction and a distance. To do this, construct any segment *KL.* Then select, in order, points *K* and *L* and choose **Transform | Mark Vector.**

Steps 1–4: Translation

Step 3 Select the interior of letter **F** and translate by your marked vector. (Choose **Transform | Translate,** make sure Marked is checked, and click OK.)

Step 4 Change the color of the translated image. Use the **Text** tool to display its label, and change the label to *Translated image.* (To change a label, double-click on the label with the **Text** tool.)

Step 5 Drag point *L* to change your vector, and observe the relationship between the translated image and the original figure.

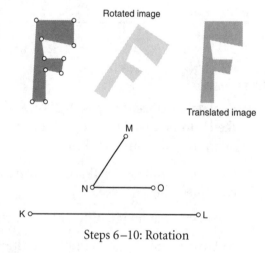

Rotated image

Translated image

Step 6 In order to rotate a shape, you need to indicate a center of rotation and an angle of rotation. Start by constructing angle *MNO* using two attached segments, as shown.

Step 7 Double-click point *N* to mark it as a center of rotation.

Step 8 To mark the angle for rotation, select, in order, points *M, N,* and *O.* Choose **Transform | Mark Angle.**

Steps 6–10: Rotation

Step 9 Select the original letter **F** and rotate by the angle you marked. (Choose **Transform | Rotate,** make sure Marked is checked, and click OK.)

(continued)

Step 10 Change the color or shading of the rotated image. Change its label to *Rotated image.*

Step 11 Drag point *M* to change your angle, and observe the relationship between the rotated image and the original figure.

Step 12 In order to reflect a shape, you need a **mirror line** (also called a **line of reflection**). Construct a line and label it *Mirror line.*

Step 13 Double-click your line to mark it as a mirror.

Step 14 Reflect the original letter **F**. (Select the interior and choose **Transform | Reflect.**) Your image may end up off the screen.

Step 15 Change the color or shading of the reflected image. Label it *Reflected image.*

Step 16 Drag your mirror line, and observe the relationship between the reflected image and the original figure.

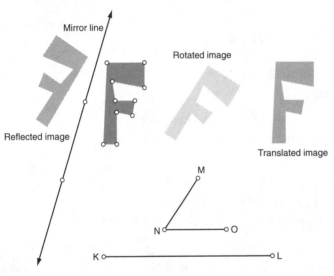

Steps 12–15: Reflection

Investigate

1. Explain whether it is possible for any of the three images in your sketch to lie exactly on top of another one. Experiment by dragging different parts of your sketch.

2. Use the original letter **F** and its *translated* image to answer these two questions.

   a. How is the image different from the original?

   b. How is the image the same as the original?

3. Answer Question 2 for the original letter **F** and its *rotated* image.

4. Answer Question 2 for the original letter **F** and its *reflected* image.

Lesson 7.2 • Properties of Isometries

In this activity you will investigate isometries on a coordinate plane. Then you'll demonstrate an important property of reflections.

Investigation 1: Transformations on a Coordinate Plane

Sketch

Step 1 In a new sketch, construct vertices of a letter by holding down the Shift key while using the **Point** tool. Choose **Construct | Interior.**

Step 2 Choose **Graph | Show Grid.** Drag the points of your letter so they fall on grid points.

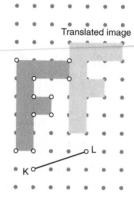

Translated image

Investigate

1. You can indicate transformations on the coordinate plane using an ordered pair rule. For example, the transformation shown follows the rule $(x, y) \rightarrow (x + 3, y + 1)$. Notice that the translation vector from point K to point L goes to the right three units and up one unit. Use the **Point** tool to construct the points to which the vertices of your letter will move by the rule $(x, y) \rightarrow (x + 3, y + 1)$. Select in pairs each corner of the letter and the point to which it will move. Then choose **Edit | Action Buttons | Movement.** Choose to have points move toward their initial destinations. When the action button appears, press it to make your letter move.

2. Change your sketch to demonstrate the transformation $(x, y) \rightarrow (-x, y)$. Explain how to create this transformation and state whether it's a translation, a reflection, or a rotation.

Investigation 2: Finding a Minimal Path

When you hit a pool ball without putting any spin on it, the ball follows a straight path toward the cushion. It bounces off the cushion at the same angle at which it came in. Can you see how this path is like a reflection?

Sketch

Step 1 In a new sketch, construct a long horizontal segment AB to represent the cushion.

Step 2 Construct points C and D on the same side of the segment. Point C represents the cue ball, and point D represents the ball you plan to hit.

Step 3 Construct $\overline{CE}$ and $\overline{ED}$, where point E is a point on $\overline{AB}$. These segments together show the path of the cue ball with one bounce off the cushion.

Step 4 Measure CE and ED.

(continued)

Step 5 Use the calculator to find the sum of these two lengths.

Step 6 Measure the incoming and outgoing angles the cue ball makes with the cushion ($\angle CEA$ and $\angle DEB$).

Step 7 Double-click $\overline{AB}$ to mark it as a mirror. Then reflect point D over $\overline{AB}$ to create point D'.

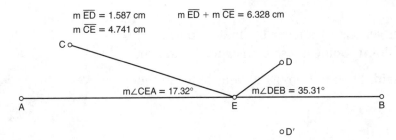

m $\overline{ED}$ = 1.587 cm   m $\overline{ED}$ + m $\overline{CE}$ = 6.328 cm
m $\overline{CE}$ = 4.741 cm

m$\angle$CEA = 17.32°   m$\angle$DEB = 35.31°

Investigate

1. Drag point E and observe the angle measurements. Locate E at the point where the cue ball should hit the cushion. Explain how you found this point.

2. Construct $\overline{CD'}$ and change its line width to dashed using the Display menu. Find its length. Explain how you can use the reflection of point D to figure out how to aim the cue ball.

3. Now drag point E again, this time watching the sum $CE + ED$. How is this total distance related to the path of the cue ball?

4. How can you use reflections to find the minimal path between two points if your path must touch a neighboring line? Write your observations as the Minimal Path Conjecture. Explain why your method works.

Lesson 7.3 • Reflections Across Lines

Demonstration

When one isometry is applied to a figure, and then another isometry is applied to the figure's image, the resulting transformation is called the **composition** of isometries. In this demonstration you'll discover what transformations result from the composition of two reflections. First you'll investigate reflections across parallel lines. Then you'll investigate reflections across lines that intersect.

Reflections Across Parallel Lines

Sketch

Step 1 Open the sketch **Reflection Demo.gsp** to the page Parallel Lines.

Step 2 Press *Reflect 1*. You'll see an image of the polygon move over to the other side of line 1 and come to rest as the mirror image of the polygon. While it's moving, imagine that it's coming out of the plane of your computer screen.

Step 3 Drag the vertices of the original polygon and drag the line. Watch the effect this has on the image.

Step 4 Press *Reflect 2*. You'll see an image of the first mirror image move over to the other side of line 2 and come to rest as the mirror image of the first image.

Step 5 Drag the vertices of the original polygon and of both images. Drag both lines. Observe how the original image and the first and second mirror images are related to each other.

Step 6 Predict which single transformation would move the original polygon to the second mirror image.

Step 7 Press the *Equivalent?* button to check your prediction.

Step 8 Press *Reset*, drag objects in the sketch around, and repeat the experiment to help you answer the following questions.

Investigate

1. What single transformation is equivalent to the composition of two reflections across parallel lines?

2. How are the direction and the distance of this transformation related to the lines?

(continued)

Reflections Across Intersecting Lines

Sketch

Step 9   Go to the page Intersecting Lines in the same sketch
(**Reflection Lines Demo.gsp.**)

Step 10   Experiment with this sketch as you did with the parallel lines sketch
to answer the following questions.

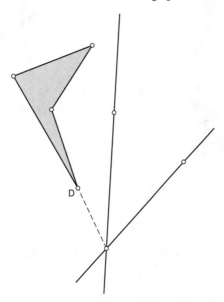

Investigate

3. What single transformation is equivalent to the composition of two
reflections across intersecting lines?

4. How is this transformation related to the angle between the lines?

Lesson 7.3 • Compositions of Transformations

When you apply one transformation to a figure, then apply another transformation to its image, the resulting transformation is called a **composition** of transformations.

Investigation 1: Reflections Across Two Parallel Lines

Sketch

Step 1 In a new sketch, construct a line and a point not on it.

Step 2 Construct a line through that point, parallel to the first line.

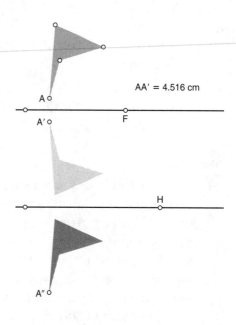

AA' = 4.516 cm

Step 3 While holding down the Shift key, use the **Point** tool to construct vertices of a polygon, all on one side of the pair of lines. Choose **Construct | Interior.**

Step 4 Double-click on the line nearest the polygon to designate it as a mirror. Select the entire polygon (including vertices) and choose **Transform | Reflect.**

Step 5 Double-click on the second line, then again choose **Transform | Reflect.**

Step 6 Select any vertex of the polygon (point *A* in the picture) and the corresponding point on the second reflection image. Choose **Measure | Distance.**

Step 7 Measure the distance between the two parallel lines by selecting one line and any point on the other line and choosing **Measure | Distance.**

Investigate

1. Drag the polygon. Also drag the lines. Describe the relationship between the two distance measurements.

2. Describe how you could transform the original polygon onto the second reflected image using only one transformation. (Try it if you have time!)

3. Combine your observations about a figure reflected across one line then across a second line parallel to the first. Write them as the Reflections Across Parallel Lines Conjecture.

(continued)

Investigation 2: Reflections Across Two Intersecting Lines

Sketch

Step 1   In a new sketch, construct any irregular polygon interior. Show one of its vertex points, and label it *A*.

Step 2   Construct two intersecting lines, each with its own two control points. Construct the point of intersection.

Step 3   Mark the line closest to the polygon as a mirror by double-clicking it, then reflect the polygon and the labeled point across this line. Change the color of the image.

Step 4   Mark the other line as a mirror, and reflect the image from the first reflection across this second line. Change the color of this second image.

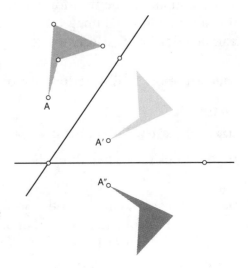

Investigate

1. Now you will investigate a single isometry that transforms the original figure onto its second image. Construct $\overline{AI}$, where point *I* is the intersection of the lines. Construct $\overline{IJ}$, where point *J* is an independent point. Double-click point *I* to mark it as a center of rotation. Measure $\angle AIJ$, then mark it as a rotation angle by reselecting the three points and choosing **Transform | Mark Angle.** Finally, choose **Transform | Rotate** to rotate your original figure by the marked angle. Drag point *J* to move the rotated image. Can you make the rotated image coincide with the second reflection image? What single isometry transforms the original figure to the second reflection image?

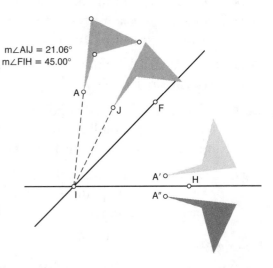

$m\angle AIJ = 21.06°$
$m\angle FIH = 45.00°$

2. Measure one of the smaller angles formed by the intersecting mirror lines. Drag point *J* so that it coincides with point *A″*. Compare the two angle measurements showing on your screen. How are they related?

3. Collect all your observations about a figure reflected across two intersecting lines. Write them as the Reflections Across Intersecting Lines Conjecture.

(continued)

Lesson 7.3 • Compositions of Transformations (continued)

Investigation 3: Glide Reflections

If you combine a translation with a reflection, you get a special two-step
isometry called a **glide reflection.**

Sketch

Step 1   In a new sketch, construct a triangle. Translate the triangle, then reflect
its translated image.

Step 2   Hide the intermediate triangle so that only the first and last
triangles are showing. The last triangle is the glide reflection
image of the first.

Step 3   Now, to continue your glide reflection, select the three vertices of the
original triangle and choose **Transform | Iterate.** A box will appear
to record where your triangle will be placed. Select the image of
point *A*, then the image of *B*, then the image of *C*. Choose 3 levels
of iteration, then click **Iterate.**

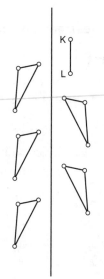

Investigate

1. Explain why it makes sense for the name of this transformation to
contain both the word *glide* and the word *reflection.*

2. Explain how a set of footprints made by a person walking on a beach
is an example of a glide reflection.

EXPLORE MORE

1. Rotate a figure by some arbitrary angle, then hide the center of
rotation. Locate two intersecting lines such that reflecting the figure
across one and then the other results in the same image as the rotation.
Show the hidden center point and describe your results.

2. Create a movement action button to have a "footprint" move to its
image under a glide reflection. (Repeatedly pressing this button will
show successive footsteps.)

3. Construct three lines that intersect in three points. Construct a polygon
and reflect it (vertices and interior) across one of the lines. Reflect the
image across a second line. Reflect this second image across the third
line. Hide the two intermediate polygons. Select the vertices of the
original figure. Choose **Transform | Iterate,** and map the vertices to
the corresponding vertices of the image, creating several additional
images. What single isometry is equivalent to three reflections?

Lesson 7.6 • Tessellations Using Only Translations

In this activity you'll learn how to construct an irregularly shaped tile based on a parallelogram. Then you'll use translations to tessellate your screen with this tile.

Investigation: Sliding Tiles

Sketch

Step 1 In a new sketch, construct $\overline{AB}$ in the lower left corner of your sketch, and construct point C just above $\overline{AB}$.

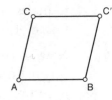

Step 2 Select point A, then point B, and choose **Transform | Mark Vector.**

Step 3 Select point C, then choose **Transform | Translate** to translate it by the marked vector.

Steps 1–4

Step 4 Construct the remaining sides of your parallelogram.

Step 5 Construct two or three connected segments from point A to point C. Call this irregular edge AC.

Step 6 Select all the segments and points of irregular edge AC and translate them by the marked vector. (Vector AB should still be marked.)

Step 5   Step 6

Now you will do the same to the other pair of parallel sides.

Step 7 Use segments to construct an irregular edge from A to B.

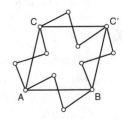

Step 8 Mark the vector from A to C.

Step 7   Steps 8 and 9

Step 9 Select all the parts of irregular edge AB and translate them by the marked vector.

Step 10 Select each of the vertices of your irregular edges in order around the figure, then choose **Construct | Polygon Interior.** This is the tile you will translate.

Step 11 Select the polygon interior and translate it by the marked vector. (You should still have vector AC marked.)

Step 12 Repeat this process until you have a column of tiles all the way up your sketch. Select alternate tiles and change their color to create a pattern.

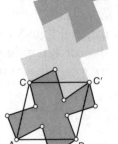

Steps 10–12

(continued)

Discovering Geometry with The Geometer's Sketchpad
©2008 Key Curriculum Press

Lesson 7.6 • Tessellations Using Only Translations (continued)

Step 13 Mark vector *AB*, then select all the polygon interiors in your column of tiles and translate them by this marked vector.

Step 14 Continue translating columns of tiles until you fill your screen. Select alternate tiles and change their color to see your tessellation.

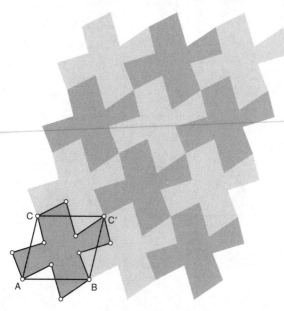

Steps 13 and 14

Step 15 Drag vertices of your original tile until you get a shape that you like or that is recognizable as some interesting form.

EXPLORE MORE

1. Animate your tessellation. (Select one or more points and choose **Display | Animate Point(s).**)

2. Make a translation tessellation that starts with a regular hexagon as the basic shape instead of a parallelogram. (The process is very similar—it just involves a third pair of sides.)

Lesson 7.7 • Tessellations That Use Rotations

The translational tessellations in Lesson 7.6 have tiles that all face in the same direction. A tessellation that uses rotations has tiles facing in different directions. The designs in a rotational tessellation have rotational symmetry about points in the tiling.

Investigation: Turning Tiles

Sketch

Step 1 In a new sketch, construct equilateral triangle *ABC* as shown. (You may have a **Custom** tool for constructing equilateral triangles. If you don't and you're having trouble figuring out how to construct an equilateral triangle, ask your teacher for ideas.)

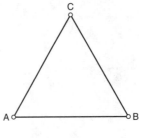

Step 1

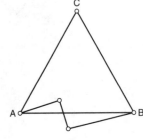

Step 2

Step 2 Construct two or three connected segments from *A* to *B*. Call this irregular edge *AB*.

Step 3 Double-click point *A* to mark it as a center. Then select all the points and segments of irregular edge *AB* and rotate it by 60° or 300° so that the other end is a vertex of the triangle. You'll find **Rotate** in the Transform menu.

Step 4 Construct midpoint *F* of side *CB*. (Select the segment, then use the Construct menu.)

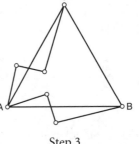

Step 3

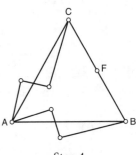

Step 4

Step 5 Construct two connected segments from *B* to *F*. Call this irregular edge *BF*.

Step 6 Double-click point *F* to mark it as a center. Then select all the points and segments of irregular edge *BF* and rotate them by 180°.

Step 7 You have finished the edges of your tile. Drag points on the edges until none of the irregular edges intersect.

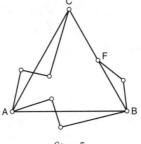

Step 5

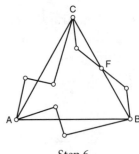

Step 6

Step 8 Select each of the vertices of your irregular edges in order around the figure, and choose **Construct | Polygon Interior.** This is the tile you will tessellate.

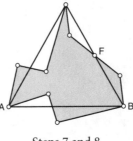

Steps 7 and 8

(continued)

Step 9 To construct a new tile, mark point *A*, *B*, *C*, or *F* as a center of rotation, and rotate the polygon (interior and vertices *A*, *B*, *C*, and *F*) by an appropriate angle. Change the color or shading of your new tile so you can see it more clearly.

Step 10 Continue this process until you have tiled a section of your sketch with at least ten tiles. Be patient, and remember that you can choose **Edit | Undo** if you make a mistake.

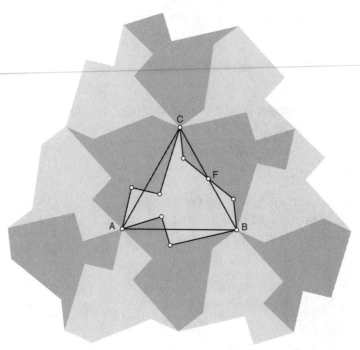

Steps 9 and 10

Step 11 Drag vertices of your original tile until you get a shape that you like or that is recognizable as some interesting form.

EXPLORE MORE

1. Use the directions on page 403 of your book to construct a tessellation based on a regular hexagon.

2. Construct a tessellation based on a parallelogram.

Lessons 7.6–7.8 • Tessellations

In Lessons 7.6–7.8, you created tessellations using translations, rotations, and glide reflections. Your challenge in this demonstration is to analyze two Sketchpad tessellations to determine the basic grid beneath each tessellation and what transformations were used to create the tile.

Sketch

Step 1 Open the sketch **Tessellation Demo.gsp** and look at the tessellation on page 1.

Step 2 Drag the vertices of the dark-shaded polygon. Observe how each vertex affects the other vertices of the tile.

Step 3 Predict which polygon (parallelogram, square, equilateral triangle, regular hexagon, kite, and so on) forms the basic grid of this tessellation.

Step 4 Press *Morph to grid* to check your prediction.

Step 5 Drag each point on each edge of the tile. As you drag each point, identify which point is the image of that point under some transformation. Try to determine what the transformation is.

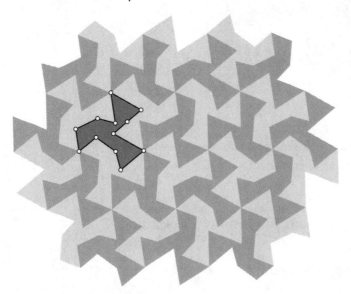

Investigate

1. What shape forms the basic grid of the tessellation?

2. What transformations were used in the tessellation?

(continued)

Sketch

Step 6 Go to page 2 in the same sketch (**Tessellation Demo.gsp**).

Step 7 Drag the vertices of the dark-shaded polygon. Observe how each vertex affects the other vertices of the tile.

Step 8 Predict which polygon (parallelogram, square, equilateral triangle, regular hexagon, kite, and so on) forms the basic grid of this tessellation.

Step 9 Press *Morph to grid* to check your prediction.

Step 10 Drag each point on each edge of the tile. As you drag each point, identify which point is the image of that point under some transformation. Try to determine what the transformation is.

Investigate

3. What shape forms the basic grid of the tessellation?

4. What transformations were used in the tessellation?

Lesson 8.1 • Areas of Rectangles and Parallelograms

The method for finding the area of a rectangle is probably familiar to you. In this lesson you'll review that method and use it to derive a method for finding the area of a parallelogram.

Investigation: Area Formula for Parallelograms

Sketch

In Steps 1–6, you'll construct a rectangle with a line through one side.

Step 1 In a new sketch, draw a horizontal segment AB.

Step 2 Construct lines perpendicular to $\overline{AB}$ through points A and B.

Step 3 Mark point C on the vertical line through A.

Step 4 Construct a line through point C parallel to $\overline{AB}$.

Step 5 Construct point D where this line intersects the vertical line through point B.

Step 6 Hide the two vertical lines, and construct segments AC and BD to complete the rectangle.

Step 7 Show the label for $\overline{AB}$ and change it to b for *base*. Show the label for $\overline{AC}$ and change it to h for *height*.

Step 8 Measure the lengths b and h.

Step 9 If these lengths are not displayed in centimeters, choose **Edit | Preferences** and choose **cm** for the distance unit.

Steps 1–7

Investigate

1. Use the calculator to create an expression in terms of b and h that you think gives the area of the rectangle. To confirm that your expression is correct, you can look at your rectangle on a grid. In the Graph menu choose **Show Grid,** and make sure **Snap Points** is checked. Hide the origin, unit point, and both axes of the coordinate system. Select the grid by clicking the mouse in one corner of it, and choose **Display | Line Width | Dotted.** Keeping $\overline{AB}$ horizontal, drag points A and B so that they snap to points on the grid. The length b should now be a whole number. Drag point C so that the top line passes through grid points. Point C won't snap to the grid, but h should be close to a whole number. If the expression you calculated is correct, it should be close to a whole number of square units. Count the number of square units in the rectangle. Is your expression correct? If not, see if you can correct it. Once the expression is correct, drag your rectangle to make sure your expression works for any rectangle. Write a formula that gives the area of a rectangle where A is the area, b is the length of the base, and h is the height of the rectangle (Rectangle Area Conjecture).

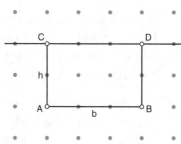

(continued)

Sketch

Now you'll construct a parallelogram with the same base and height as the rectangle.

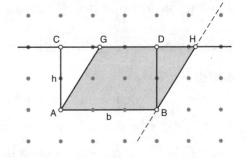

Step 10 Continuing in the same sketch, construct $\overline{AG}$, where point G is a point on the line through the top of the rectangle.

Step 11 Translate $\overline{AG}$ (including point G) along the vector from A to B.

Step 12 Change the name of G' to H.

Step 13 Measure AG and BH.

Step 14 Construct quadrilateral interior $AGHB$.

Investigate

2. As you drag point G, what measurements change?

3. What measurements stay the same as you drag point G?

4. Is it possible to drag point G so that the parallelogram fills in the rectangle?

5. Without measuring the area of the parallelogram, do you think this changes when you drag point G? After you have made your prediction, measure the area of the polygon interior to check it. Write down your observation.

6. Write a formula for the area of a parallelogram (Parallelogram Area Conjecture).

EXPLORE MORE

1. In the figure above, what do you notice about $\triangle ACG$ and $\triangle BDH$? Draw a parallelogram on a piece of paper. Cut it out, then show how you can cut it into two pieces that can be arranged to form a rectangle. Explain how this demonstrates the Parallelogram Area Conjecture.

2. Use symmetry to construct a rectangle: Construct a right triangle, then rotate it about the midpoint of the hypotenuse. Can you construct a parallelogram with the same base and height?

Lesson 8.2 • Areas of Triangles and Trapezoids Demonstration

This demonstration shows how triangles and trapezoids are related to a shape whose area you already know how to find. From this relationship, you'll derive formulas for the areas of triangles and trapezoids.

Triangle Area

Sketch

Step 1 Open the sketch **Triangle Trap Area Demo.gsp** to the page Triangle Area.

Step 2 Drag parts of the triangle to see how they behave and how they affect the measurements in the sketch. To change the triangle's height, drag the blue line through the top vertex up and down.

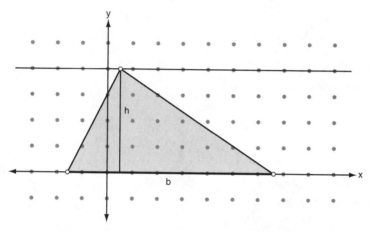

Step 3 Press *Double Triangle*.

Step 4 Drag different parts of the sketch and observe how the doubled triangle compares to the original triangle.

Investigate

1. How can you change the shape of the triangle without changing its area? Why doesn't the area change in this case?

2. Describe two ways in which you can change the area of the triangle.

3. What kind of shape is formed when you double the triangle? What is the area of this shape in terms of *b* and *h*?

4. What is the area of the triangle in terms of *b* and *h*?

(continued)

Trapezoid Area

Sketch

Step 5 Go to the page Trapezoid Area in the same sketch
(**Triangle Trap Area Demo.gsp**).

Step 6 Drag parts of the trapezoid to see how they behave and how they
affect the measurements in the sketch. To change the trapezoid's
height, drag the blue line through base b_1 up and down.

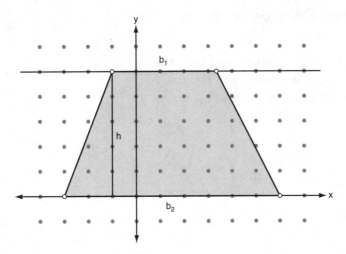

Step 7 Press *Double Trapezoid*.

Step 8 Drag different parts of the sketch and observe how the doubled
trapezoid compares to the original trapezoid.

Investigate

5. How can you change the shape of the trapezoid without changing its
   area? Why doesn't the area change in this case?

6. Describe three ways in which you can change the area of the trapezoid.

7. What kind of shape is formed when you double the trapezoid? What is
   the area of this shape in terms of b_1, b_2, and h?

8. What is the area of the trapezoid in terms of b_1, b_2, and h?

Lesson 8.2 • Areas of Triangles, Trapezoids, and Kites

In this lesson you will discover formulas for the areas of triangles, trapezoids, and kites.

Investigation 1: Area Formula for Triangles

Sketch

Step 1 In a new sketch, choose **Edit | Preferences** to make sure the distance unit is centimeters.

Step 2 In the Graph menu choose **Show Grid,** and make sure **Snap Points** is checked. Hide the origin, unit point, and both axes of the coordinate system. Select the grid by clicking the mouse in one corner of it, and choose **Display | Line Width | Dotted.**

Step 3 Construct any triangle CDE with its vertices at grid points.

Step 4 Construct the midpoint F of $\overline{DE}$.

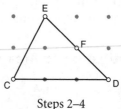

Steps 2–4

Step 5 Double-click on point F to mark it as a center of rotation.

Step 6 Select point C, $\overline{CE}$, and $\overline{CD}$, and choose **Transform | Rotate.** Rotate by a fixed angle of 180°.

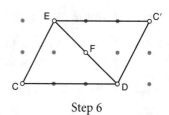

Step 6

Investigate

1. Drag the vertices of your original triangle. What kind of quadrilateral is $CDC'E$?

2. What is the formula for the area of quadrilateral $CDC'E$ in terms of its base and height?

3. What are the base, height, and area of $\triangle CDE$ compared to the entire quadrilateral?

4. Write your findings as the Triangle Area Conjecture.

Investigation 2: Area Formula for Trapezoids

Sketch

Step 1 Follow Steps 1 and 2 from Investigation 1.

Step 2 Construct $\overline{AB}$.

Step 3 Mark point C and construct a line through point C parallel to $\overline{AB}$.

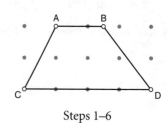

Steps 1–6

Step 4 Mark point D on the line.

Step 5 Hide $\overleftrightarrow{CD}$.

Step 6 Construct $\overline{AC}$, $\overline{CD}$, and $\overline{DB}$ to complete trapezoid $ABDC$.

Step 7 Show the labels of $\overline{AB}$ and $\overline{CD}$ and change them to b_1 and b_2.

(continued)

Investigate

1. Construct the midpoint of one of the nonparallel sides and rotate the trapezoid 180° about this midpoint. What kind of shape do you have?

2. How do the base lengths and height of this doubled trapezoid compare with the original?

3. Based on your observations, write a formula for the area A of a trapezoid using b_1 for one base, b_2 for the second base, and h for the height. Write your findings as the Trapezoid Area Conjecture.

Investigation 3: Area Formula for Kites

Sketch

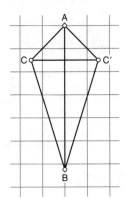

Step 1 In a new sketch, choose **Graph | Show Grid.** Then select and hide the axes and the unit control points.

Step 2 Construct $\overline{AB}$. This will be one diagonal of your kite.

Step 3 Double-click $\overline{AB}$ to mark it as a mirror for a reflection.

Step 4 Construct point C, not on $\overline{AB}$. While it's selected, choose **Transform | Reflect** to construct point C'.

Step 5 Construct $\overline{CB}$, $\overline{BC'}$, $\overline{C'A}$, and $\overline{AC}$ to complete kite $ACBC'$.

Step 6 Construct $\overline{CC'}$, the other diagonal of the kite.

Investigate

1. Recall some of the properties of a kite. The diagonal connecting the vertex angles of the kite divides the kite into two congruent triangles. It is also the perpendicular bisector of the other diagonal. Can you calculate the area of a kite if you know the lengths of the two diagonals? Write a formula and use Sketchpad to test it. Write your findings as a conjecture (Kite Area Conjecture).

EXPLORE MORE

1. Construct a triangle or a trapezoid whose perimeter you can change without changing the area.

2. Find a formula for the area of any quadrilateral.

Lesson 8.4 • Areas of Regular Polygons

In this lesson you will discover a formula for the area of any regular polygon. Recall that a regular polygon is equilateral and equiangular.

Investigation: Pentagons and Triangles

Sketch

Step 1 Open a sketch that has **Custom** tools for drawing regular polygons.

Step 2 Open a new sketch. Use a **Custom** tool to construct a regular pentagon.

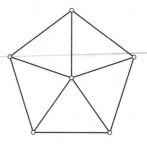

Step 3 Delete the polygon interior if there is one.

Step 4 Construct the pentagon's center if it doesn't already have one.

Step 5 Construct segments to connect the vertices to the center.

Investigate

1. How many triangles did you form in the construction?

2. Are the triangles congruent? Explain.

3. What is the formula in terms of b and h for the area of one of the triangles?

4. The **apothem** of a regular polygon is a perpendicular segment from the center of the polygon to a side of the polygon. This segment is also the altitude of each of the congruent triangles that form the polygon. Write a formula for the area of one of the triangles of your pentagon in terms of the apothem a and the length of a side s.

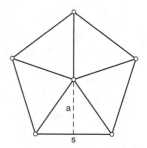

5. Use your formula from Question 4 to write a formula for the area of a regular pentagon in terms of the apothem a and the length of a side s.

6. Use your **Custom** tools to construct other regular polygons. How many congruent triangles can you make by connecting the vertices to the center of a regular polygon with n sides?

7. Write a formula for the area of any regular n-gon, using A for the area, a for the apothem, s for the length of one side, and n for the number of sides (Regular Polygon Area Conjecture).

8. Let P be the perimeter of a regular n-gon. Rewrite the formula in Question 7, substituting P for part of the formula. Add this formula to your conjecture.

EXPLORE MORE

Construct an apothem in a regular polygon. Make measurements and use the calculator to create an expression that gives the area of the polygon. Construct the polygon interior and measure its area to confirm that the expression you created works.

Lesson 8.5 • Areas of Circles

The formula for the area of a circle can be derived from the formula for the area of a regular polygon. In this activity you will experiment with a sketch that demonstrates this.

Investigation: Area Formula for Circles

Sketch

Step 1 Open the sketch **To a Circle.gsp.**

Step 2 Drag or animate point *drag* along the segment. (To animate the point, press *Animate*. To stop the animation, press again.)

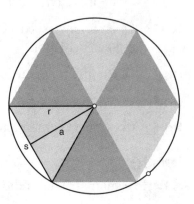

Investigate

1. What do you observe about the area of the inscribed regular polygon compared to the area of the circle as the number of sides of the polygon increases?

2. What is the formula for the circumference C of the circle in terms of r?

3. What is the formula for the area of the inscribed polygon in terms of a (apothem) and p (perimeter)?

4. As the number of sides of the regular polygon increases, the apothem becomes close to the radius, and the perimeter of the polygon approaches the circumference of the circle. In the formula you wrote for Question 3, substitute C for p and r for a.

5. Simplify your answer to Question 4 to write a formula for the area A of a circle with radius r (Circle Area Conjecture).

Explore More

Use Sketchpad to construct this figure. What is the ratio of the area of the circle to the area of the square? Use algebra to explain your results.

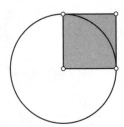

Lesson 9.1 • Three Squares   Demonstration

The Pythagorean Theorem describes a special relationship among the legs and the hypotenuse of any right triangle. This demonstration shows how squares constructed on the legs of a right triangle can be dissected into pieces that fit into the square on the hypotenuse.

Sketch

Step 1 Open the sketch **Three Squares Demo.gsp.**

Step 2 Drag each vertex of the triangle and observe how the shapes change.

Step 3 Press the buttons *Move Square on b* and *Move Square on a.*

Step 4 Drag each vertex of the triangle again.

Step 5 Press *Reset* and repeat the experiment.

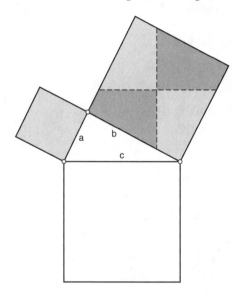

Investigate

1. If the short leg of the triangle has length *a*, what is the area of the square constructed on that leg?

2. If the long leg of the triangle has length *b*, what is the area of the square constructed on that leg?

3. If the hypotenuse of the triangle has length *c*, what is the area of the square constructed on it in terms of *c*?

4. What did pressing the *Move Square* buttons demonstrate?

5. What is the area of the square constructed on the hypotenuse in terms of lengths *a* and *b*?

6. Write an equation that relates lengths *a*, *b*, and *c*.

Lesson 9.1 • The Theorem of Pythagoras

The Pythagorean Theorem states a relationship between the areas of squares constructed on the three sides of a right triangle. In this investigation you'll explore this relationship in two ways: first, by measuring and calculating and, second, by cutting the squares on the two legs of the right triangle and arranging them to fit in the square on the hypotenuse.

Investigation: The Three Sides of a Right Triangle

Sketch

Step 1 In a new sketch, construct $\overline{AB}$.

Step 2 Construct the midpoint C of $\overline{AB}$.

Step 3 Construct a circle centered at C with radius endpoint B.

Step 4 Construct $\overline{AD}$ and $\overline{BD}$, where point D is a point on the circle.

Step 5 Hide the circle and the midpoint. Drag points A, B, and D to be sure your triangle stays a right triangle.

Step 6 Open a sketch that has a **Custom** tool for creating a square. This can be either a sketch you have made yourself or the sketch **Polygons.gsp**.

Step 7 Construct squares on the outsides of the triangle.

Step 8 Measure the areas of the three squares.

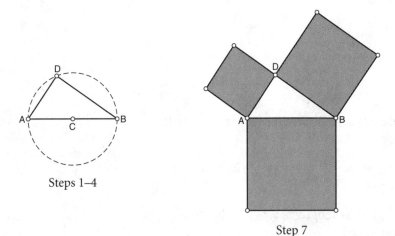

Steps 1–4

Step 7

Investigate

1. Drag vertices of the triangle and look for a relationship among the areas of the three squares. Use the calculator to confirm your observation. State a conjecture about these three areas (The Pythagorean Theorem).

(continued)

Discovering Geometry with The Geometer's Sketchpad
©2008 Key Curriculum Press

Sketch

You can use dissection puzzles to demonstrate that figures have equal areas without measuring them. Continue in your sketch to create a dissection that demonstrates the Pythagorean Theorem.

Step 9 Delete the square interiors on the longer leg and on the hypotenuse, but not on the smaller leg.

Step 10 Find point *O*, the center of the square on the longer leg, by constructing the diagonals.

Step 11 Hide the diagonals.

Step 12 Construct a line through point *O* parallel to hypotenuse *AB*.

Step 13 Construct a line through point *O* perpendicular to hypotenuse *AB*.

Step 14 Construct the four points where these two new lines intersect the sides of the square.

Step 15 Construct the polygon interiors of the four quadrilaterals in the larger square. Give them all different colors.

Step 16 Hide the lines.

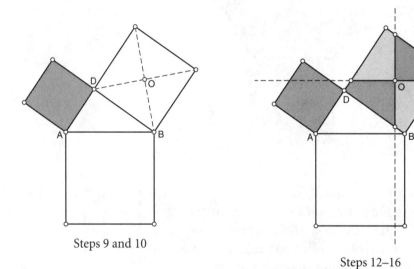

Steps 9 and 10

Steps 12–16

Investigate

2. You should now have a five-piece puzzle. One piece is the square on the small leg, and four pieces form the square on the longer leg. The object of the puzzle is to arrange these five pieces to fit in the square on the hypotenuse. In turn, select each of the five interiors, choose **Cut** from the Edit menu, then choose **Paste.** Hide any extraneous points. Your five pieces are now free to be moved. Click in a blank area of your sketch to deselect everything, then drag each piece and find a way to fit all the pieces in the square on the hypotenuse. When you finish, draw the solution on your paper. (That is, draw a square and sketch how the five pieces fit into the square.)

3. Explain how this dissection demonstrates the Pythagorean Theorem.

Lesson 9.2 • The Converse of the Pythagorean Theorem

To investigate the converse of the Pythagorean Theorem, you can construct
squares on the sides of an ordinary triangle, then manipulate the triangle
until the squares satisfy the theorem.

Investigation: Is the Converse True?

Sketch

Step 1 In a new sketch, construct any triangle *ABC*. It should not be a right
triangle.

Step 2 Construct squares and their interiors on the outsides of the triangle's
sides. Use a **Custom** tool such as 4/Square (By Edge) from the
sketch **Polygons.gsp.**

Step 3 Measure the areas of the three squares.

Step 4 Calculate the sum of the two smaller areas.

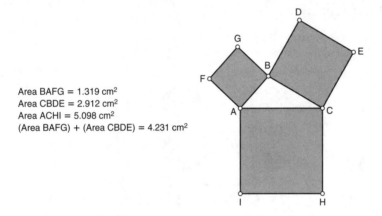

Area BAFG = 1.319 cm²
Area CBDE = 2.912 cm²
Area ACHI = 5.098 cm²
(Area BAFG) + (Area CBDE) = 4.231 cm²

Investigate

1. Drag a vertex of the triangle until the sum of the areas of the
   two squares approximately equals the area of the third square.
   What kind of triangle do you have? Measure an angle to confirm
   your observation; then write a conjecture (Converse of the
   Pythagorean Theorem).

2. Open the sketch **Triple Checker.gsp.** A set of three positive
   integers that satisfies the Pythagorean formula is called a
   Pythagorean triple. One such set is 3-4-5, because
   $3^2 + 4^2 = 5^2$. Drag vertex *B*, then *A*, to find other sets of
   Pythagorean triples.

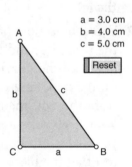

a = 3.0 cm
b = 4.0 cm
c = 5.0 cm

Reset

Lesson 9.3 • Two Special Right Triangles

In this lesson you'll discover shortcuts that will enable you to find side lengths quickly in two types of special right triangles. The first special triangle you'll investigate is half a square. Then you'll investigate the right triangle that is half an equilateral triangle.

Investigation 1: Isosceles Right Triangles

Sketch

Step 1   In a new sketch, construct a square *ABCD*. (Use a **Custom** tool.)

Step 2   Construct diagonal *CA*.

Step 3   Hide the square's interior, if it has one.

Step 4   Change the line width of $\overline{CD}$ and $\overline{DA}$ to dashed.

Step 5   Use the square tool to construct squares on the sides of right triangle *ABC*.

Step 6   Construct one diagonal in each of the smaller squares as shown below.

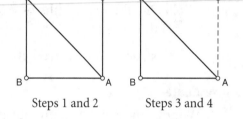

Steps 1 and 2   Steps 3 and 4

Investigate

1. Triangle *ABC* is an isosceles right triangle. Without measuring, figure out the measure of each angle in an isosceles right triangle. Explain how you found each measure.

2. The diagonals you constructed in the smaller squares may help you see a relationship between the smaller squares and the square on the hypotenuse. If each of the smaller squares has area x^2, what is the area of the large square? Confirm your conjecture both by measuring the areas and by dissecting the smaller squares into pieces that can be cut and pasted to fill the larger square.

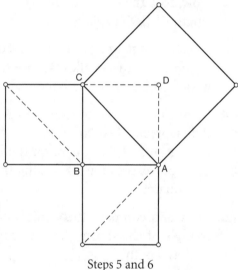

Steps 5 and 6

3. Copy and complete this conjecture: In an isosceles right triangle, if the legs have length *x*, then the hypotenuse has length _____ (Isosceles Right Triangle Conjecture).

(continued)

Investigation 2: 30°-60°-90° Triangles

Sketch

Step 1 In a new sketch, construct an equilateral triangle *ABC*. Use a **Custom** tool or construct it from scratch.

Step 2 Construct the midpoint *D* of $\overline{AB}$ and median $\overline{CD}$.

Step 3 Hide the triangle's interior, if necessary.

Step 4 Change the line widths of $\overline{AB}$ and $\overline{AC}$ to dashed.

Step 5 Construct $\overline{BD}$ and make its line width thin.

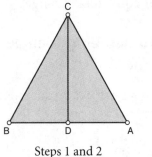 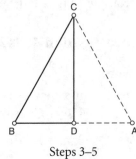

Steps 1 and 2   Steps 3–5

Investigate

1. Without measuring, figure out the measure of each angle in △*BCD*. Explain how you found each measure.

2. How does the length of $\overline{BC}$ compare with the length of $\overline{BD}$? Explain why.

3. Construct squares on the three sides of △*BCD* as shown. If the smallest square has area x^2, what is the area of the largest square?

4. Using your answer to Question 3 and the Pythagorean Theorem, write an expression for the area of the square on the longer leg. Test your expression by finding the areas of the squares.

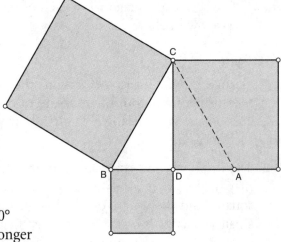

5. Copy and complete this conjecture: In a 30°-60°-90° triangle, if the shorter leg has length *x*, then the longer leg has length _____ and the hypotenuse has length _____ (30°-60°-90° Triangle Conjecture).

Exploration • A Right Triangle Fractal   Demonstration

This fractal is based on a right triangle. Relationships among the areas of the branches can be calculated using the Pythagorean Theorem.

Sketch

Step 1 Open the sketch **Right Triangle Fractal Demo.gsp.**

Step 2 Drag point C around the semicircle with endpoints A and B. What kind of triangle is $\triangle ABC$? How do you know?

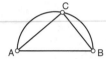

Step 3 Press the buttons *Hide Semicircle* and *Show Squares.*

Step 4 What you see is an iterated construction, where the number of iterations is controlled by the parameter *Stage*, which is under the largest square. Select *Stage* and press the plus ($+$) and minus ($-$) keys on your keyboard to increase and decrease its value.

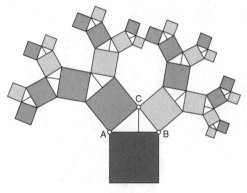

Stage = 3

Investigate

1. Use the plus ($+$) and minus ($-$) keys on your keyboard to set *Stage* to 0. Use the Pythagorean Theorem to write an equation relating the areas of the three squares.

2. What is happening with each new iteration?

3. How much shaded area is added when you go from Stage 0 to Stage 1? From Stage 1 to Stage 2? Make a conjecture about how much shaded area is added at any new stage of the construction.

4. Increase *Stage* to 11. Recall from the Chapter 2 Exploration Patterns in Fractals that one characteristic of fractals is *self-similarity.* Can you locate a part of the construction that looks just like the whole thing?

Exploration • A Pythagorean Fractal

In this activity you'll build a fractal based on a right triangle and use the Pythagorean Theorem to find relationships among branches of the fractal.

Sketch

Step 1   In a new sketch, construct horizontal segment AB.

Step 2   Construct the midpoint M of $\overline{AB}$, and then construct circle MB. Hide point M.

Step 3   Construct a semicircle above $\overline{AB}$, with $\overline{AB}$ as its diameter. (Select the circle and points A and B, and choose **Construct | Arc On Circle.** If you constructed the semicircle below $\overline{AB}$, then undo that construction and do it again, this time selecting A and B in a different order.) Hide the full circle.

Step 4   Construct point C on the semicircle, and construct segments AC and BC. Hide the semicircle.

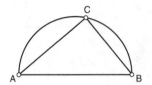

Investigate

1. What kind of triangle is $\triangle ABC$? How do you know? Drag vertices of the triangle to confirm your answer.

Sketch

Step 5   Open a sketch that has a **Custom** tool for creating a square. This can be either a sketch you have made yourself or the sketch **Polygons.gsp.**

Step 6   Construct square $ACDE$ on $\overline{AC}$ and square $CBFG$ on $\overline{CB}$. Make sure both squares are constructed outside of $\triangle ABC$.

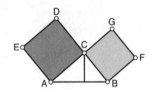

Step 7   Construct the altitude from point C to $\overline{AB}$.

Step 8   Choose **Graph | New Parameter** to create a new parameter named *Stage*. Set its value to 3.

Step 9   Select, in order, points A and B, and the parameter *Stage*. With these objects selected, hold down the shift key and choose **Transform | Iterate To Depth.** With the dialog box open, click on points in the sketch to designate that A maps to G and B maps to F. Before closing the dialog box, choose **Add New Map** from the Structure pop-up menu, and map points A and B to outer points of the other square. If your iterated figure doesn't look similar to the one shown, experiment with the order in which you map the points.

Step 10   Construct a square below $\triangle ABC$, on $\overline{AB}$.

(continued)

Discovering Geometry with The Geometer's Sketchpad
©2008 Key Curriculum Press

Exploration • A Pythagorean Fractal (continued)

Step 11 Hide all points except *A, B,* and *C.* Your fractal should now look similar to the one shown below.

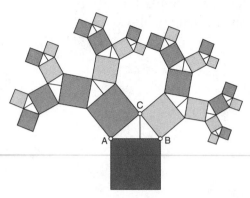

Stage = 3.00

Investigate

2. Select the parameter *Stage* and press the minus (−) key on your keyboard until its value is 0. Use the Pythagorean Theorem to write an equation relating the areas of the three squares.

3. Select the parameter *Stage* and press the plus (+) key on your keyboard to set its value to 1. When you go from Stage 0 to Stage 1, you add four squares to your construction. How much shaded area is added, in total?

4. How much shaded area is added when you go from Stage 1 to Stage 2?

5. Use your answers to Questions 3 and 4 to determine how much shaded area is added at any new stage of the construction.

6. A true fractal exists only after an infinite number of stages. If you could build a true fractal based on the construction in this activity, what would be its total area?

Explore more

1. Consider the new squares that were created from Stage 0 to Stage 1. What do all of these squares have in common? How about all of the new squares that were created from Stage 1 to Stage 2? From Stage 2 to Stage 3? Use inductive reasoning to make a conjecture about the new squares created at any stage.

2. Drag point *C* so △*ABC* is very noticeably scalene, and set *Stage* to 1. Observe just the squares that were created from Stage 0 to Stage 1 (the outer-most squares on the "tree"). How many different sizes of squares are there? How many squares are there of each size? Answer these questions again for Stage 2 and Stage 3. Then use inductive reasoning to answer the questions for any new stage.

Lesson 9.5 • Distance in Coordinate Geometry

In this lesson you'll use the Pythagorean Theorem to derive a formula for the distance between any two points in a coordinate plane. Then you'll use that formula to derive the equation for a circle.

Investigation 1: The Distance Formula

Sketch
Open the sketch **Coordinate Distance.gsp.**

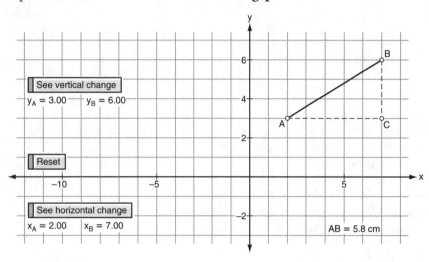

Investigate

1. Use the Pythagorean Theorem to write an expression relating *AC*, *BC*, and *AB*.

2. Write an expression for *AC* using coordinates of points. Use the action buttons as you wish. Drag points *A* and *B* around the coordinate plane to check your ideas.

3. Find an expression for *BC*.

4. Write an expression for *AB* using coordinates of points *A* and *B*.

5. Enter your expression for *AB* in the Sketchpad calculator to see whether it matches the measured value of *AB*. (Click on the ^ key for exponents. For the square root function, use **sqrt** in the Functions pop-up menu on the calculator. Don't forget to use parentheses where needed.) Once you've found an expression that seems to work consistently, write it as a conjecture (Distance Formula).

(continued)

Discovering Geometry with The Geometer's Sketchpad

Investigation 2: The Equation of a Circle

Sketch

Step 1 In the same sketch (**Coordinate Distance.gsp**), construct a circle centered at point A using B as a radius endpoint.

Step 2 Measure the equation of the circle.

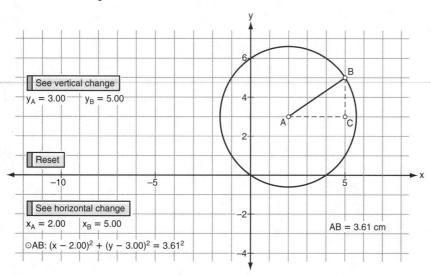

Investigate

1. Drag point A or point B and look for relationships between the circle's equation and the coordinates of the center and the length of the radius. Write a conjecture about the equation of a circle (Equation of a Circle).

2. Play a game with a partner to practice finding equations of a circle. To play, draw several circles in a sketch. Make sure no labels are showing. Measure the circles' equations. Have your partner match equations with circles. Drag a circle to check the matched equation. If the equation changes when the circle moves, then the match is correct.

Lesson 11.1 • Similarity

Figures are **similar** if they look the same. Similar figures have the same shape, but not necessarily the same size. In this investigation you'll dilate shapes to discover principles of **similarity.** You'll use your discoveries to write a definition of **similar polygons.**

Investigation: Similar Polygons

Sketch

Step 1 In a new sketch, construct any polygon.

Step 2 Construct a point outside the polygon, and double-click it to mark it as a center of dilation.

Step 3 Construct two segments of different lengths outside your polygon. Select them both and choose **Transform | Mark Segment Ratio.**

Step 4 Select your entire polygon and dilate by the marked ratio by choosing **Transform | Dilate.**

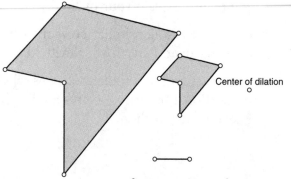
Center of dilation

Investigate

Now you can compare your two similar figures.

1. First drag the center of dilation. Also change the lengths of the two segments that define the ratio. How do the similar polygons change? How can you make the dilated image coincide with the original figure?

2. Construct any line segment outside the polygons, and double-click it to mark it as a mirror for reflection. Select the dilated image and reflect it. This reflected image is congruent to the dilated image and is also similar to the original image. Experiment with the ratio segments again. Is it possible for similar figures to be congruent?

3. Measure the ratio of the segments that define the dilation ratio. Measure the ratios of some corresponding side lengths of your polygons. How do these ratios compare?

4. Measure some corresponding angles in these figures. How do these angles compare?

5. Write a definition of similar polygons.

6. Copy and complete this conjecture: If one polygon is a dilated image of another polygon, then _____ (Dilation Similarity Conjecture).

(continued)

EXPLORE MORE

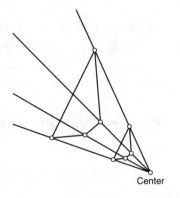

Center

1. Construct rays from the point marked as the center through each vertex of your original polygon.

   a. What other point does each ray pass through?

   b. How does the distance between the center and a vertex of the first polygon compare to the distance between the center and the corresponding vertex of the second polygon?

2. Construct a pair of similar triangles without using the **Dilate** command. Explain your method.

3. Construct two nonsimilar polygons whose corresponding angles are congruent. Explain your method.

4. Construct two nonsimilar polygons whose corresponding sides are proportional but whose corresponding angles are not congruent. Explain your method.

Lesson 11.2 • Similar Triangles

In Chapter 4, you found shortcuts for determining whether two triangles are congruent. In this activity you will find some shortcuts for determining whether two triangles are similar. It's not always convenient to check all three pairs of angles for congruence and all three pairs of sides for proportionality. It's handy to know which smaller sets of corresponding parts you can check instead.

Investigation: Finding Similarity Conjectures

Sketch

Step 1 Open the sketch **Similarity Shortcuts.gsp.**

Step 2 Choose which shortcut you'd like to investigate—AA, SSS, SSA, or SAS—and go to that page.

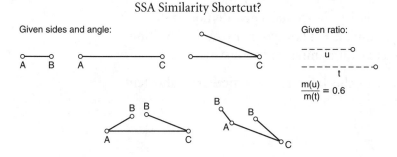

SSA Similarity Shortcut?

Investigate

1. Drag the vertices of the givens and observe how they affect the triangles (or fractured triangles) in your sketch.

   a. If your givens include any angles, explain the connection between the given angle(s) and the triangles (or fractured triangles).

   b. If your givens include any sides, explain the connection between the given side(s) and the triangles (or fractured triangles).

   c. If your givens include a ratio, explain the connection between the given ratio and the triangles (or fractured triangles).

2. If any triangles below the givens are fractured, drag parts of your sketch until you have two complete triangles. Do the triangles appear to be similar triangles?

3. To check for similarity, measure pairs of corresponding angles and ratios of corresponding sides. (To measure the ratio, select the shorter of the corresponding sides, then the longer, and choose **Measure | Ratio.**) Use your measurements to decide whether your triangles are similar.

(continued)

4. If you have already created a pair of nonsimilar triangles, go to Question 5. Otherwise, continue your search for a counterexample. Change your givens to try at least one more case. Do your best to create a pair of nonsimilar triangles with the given constraints. Record your results.

5. If you are quite sure you can't find a counterexample, you may have discovered a similarity shortcut. Record your results as a conjecture. If you have found a counterexample, draw a sketch of the counterexample and explain why your similarity shortcut doesn't work.

6. Make sure you collect and record all the similarity conjectures. To do this, you may need to test some of the sample sketches yourself or gather information collected by your classmates.

EXPLORE MORE

1. Construct a pair of triangles that are constrained by the requirements of one of the similarity shortcuts. Then demonstrate that these triangles are always similar. Explain your method in writing or save a clearly captioned sketch containing your construction.

2. Explain why it is not necessary to check for an SAA similarity shortcut or an ASA similarity shortcut.

Exploration • Dilation Design

This sketch contains a list of action buttons for steps used in constructing a dilation design. Pressing each button reveals a part of the design. If you go through the steps out of order, the results will probably not be so impressive!

Sketch

Step 1 Open the sketch **Dilation Design Demo.gsp.**

Step 2 Press *Construct circle and radius.* Adjust the circle however you wish, but don't hide the labels, because later steps refer to them.

Step 3 The button *Rotate B, construct ray* rotates the point B counterclockwise about A by 45° and constructs $\overrightarrow{AB'}$.

Step 4 Press *Construct circle through C on ray* to put a point C on the ray outside the original circle and to construct another circle, with center A and through C. You can adjust this circle by dragging C.

Step 5 The next button hides the ray and constructs segment AC.

Step 6 The button *Rotate AC by 45 degrees* rotates the radius counterclockwise, making a sector of the larger circle.

Step 7 To get a point inside that sector but outside the original sector, press *Construct and connect point D.* Segments from D to C and C' also appear. Drag point D and observe what happens. You can drag D anywhere on the sketch, but at first try keeping it in this region.

Step 8 Press *Dilate angle by circles' scale factor.* A dilation of the angle at point D appears inside the original circle.

Step 9 Press *Construct polygon interiors* to construct two triangles and a quadrilateral between the angle and its dilation.

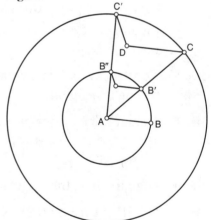

Step 10 Press *Dilate polygon interiors twice* to make two copies of those interiors, each dilated from the previous by the circles' scale factor. Dragging points D or B can help show what happened.

Step 11 The full figure appears when you press the next button.

Investigate

1. What symmetry does the figure have for various locations of point D?

2. How does dragging point C away from A change the scale factor? What effect does that have on the design?

3. What happens when point C is dragged inside the original circle? Why? (You may want to start over and do this dragging between Steps 7 and 8.)

Lesson 11.3 • Indirect Measurement with Similar Triangles

You can use similar triangles to calculate the heights of objects you are
unable to measure directly.

Investigation 1: Mirror, Mirror

Sketch

Step 1   In a new sketch, construct a horizontal line. This will
represent the ground.

Step 2   Construct two points on the line. These will represent the
places where your feet and the tree each meet the ground.

Step 3   Select both points and the line, and choose
Construct | Perpendicular Lines.

Steps 1–5

Step 4   Use these perpendicular lines to construct segments that start
at the ground and are perpendicular to the ground. Hide the lines.

Step 5   Label the two perpendicular segments. Change the labels so one
segment is named after you and the other is called *Tall tree*. Adjust
the heights so that the tree is much taller than you.

Step 6   Construct another point on the line, between you
and the tree. This will represent a mirror. Construct
a segment from the top of the tree to the mirror,
representing the beginning of a light ray's path.

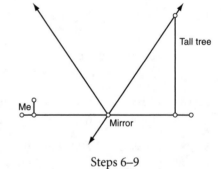

Steps 6–9

Step 7   Construct a line from the top of the tree through
the mirror. Construct a point on this line, below
the ground.

Step 8   Construct a ray starting at the mirror and going
through this point.

Step 9   Double-click on the ground to mark it as a line of reflection, and
reflect the ray. The image represents the continuation of the path
of the light ray.

Step 10   Hide the line, the original ray, and the point below the ground.

Step 11   Because in reality the tree is very tall, you cannot measure its height.
However, you can measure your own height and the distances from
the mirror to you and from the mirror to the tree. Measure these
three lengths in your sketch.

Investigate

1. Move the mirror along the ground. What do you notice?

2. Adjust segment *Me* so that the beam of light passes through your "eye"
(at the top of the segment representing you). How do the two triangles
appear to relate?

(continued)

Discovering Geometry with The Geometer's Sketchpad
©2008 Key Curriculum Press

Lesson 11.3 • Indirect Measurement with Similar Triangles (continued)

3. Measure some angles and ratios. Do the measurements support your conjecture?

4. How can you use your observations to find the height of the tree?

Investigation 2: The Shadow Knows

If the day is sunny, you can find the height of a tall object outdoors by measuring shadows.

Sketch

Step 1 In a new sketch, construct a horizontal line. This will represent the ground.

Step 2 Construct two points on the line. These will represent the places where your feet and the tree each meet the ground.

Step 3 Select both points and the line, and choose **Construct | Perpendicular Lines.**

Step 4 Use these perpendicular lines to construct segments that start at the ground and are perpendicular to the ground. Hide the lines.

Step 5 Label the two perpendicular segments. Change the labels so one segment is named after you and the other is called *Tall tree.* Adjust the heights so that the tree is much taller than you.

Step 6 Draw a slanted line through the point at the top of your head and a point on the ground. Use the Display menu to change this line width to dashed. This line represents a ray of sunlight as it makes a shadow on the ground.

Step 7 Because the sun is so far away, its rays are essentially parallel. Construct a segment parallel to the dashed line that passes through the top of the tree. (Select the point and the dashed line, and choose **Construct | Parallel Line.**)

Step 8 Construct the point where the dashed line through the treetop intersects the ground. Now hide the line that represents the ground, and construct segments to represent the shadows of both you and the tree.

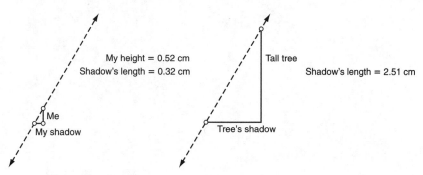

My height = 0.52 cm
Shadow's length = 0.32 cm

Tall tree
Shadow's length = 2.51 cm

Me
My shadow

Tree's shadow

(continued)

Step 9 Change the width of these shadows to thick. Also label the shadows after their objects.

Step 10 Because in reality the tree is very tall, you cannot measure its height. However, you can measure the length of the shadows and your own height. Measure these three lengths in your sketch.

Investigate

1. How are the two triangles in your sketch related? Explain how you know.

2. Your model drawing is a scale drawing. (You are actually much taller than the segment on your screen!) Drag the segment that represents you on your screen until its length represents your height in some way. For example, the creator of the sketch shown on the previous page is 52 in. tall, so she made a segment that is 0.52 cm long. Drag your tree to a good height and slant the sun's rays to a reasonable angle. Using *only* the three measurements you have already made, figure out the height of the tree. Show and explain all your work.

3. Because this is only a model, you can check your reasoning in Question 2 by measuring the height of the tree. Find this length. How well do your calculations match this measurement?

4. Suppose you measured the shadows of two straight objects at different times of day. Is it possible for the objects and their shadows to create similar triangles?

Lesson 11.4 • Corresponding Parts of Similar Triangles

You know that corresponding angles in a pair of similar triangles are congruent. You also know that corresponding sides are proportional. What about other corresponding parts of triangles, such as altitudes, medians, and angle bisectors?

Before you investigate this question, follow these steps to construct a pair of similar triangles.

Investigation 1: Corresponding Parts

Sketch

In Steps 1–7, you'll construct a pair of similar triangles.

Step 1 In a new sketch, construct any triangle *ABC*.

Step 2 Construct a triangle congruent to △*ABC*. To do this, select the entire triangle and translate it by a reasonable distance and angle to keep it on your screen. (For example, an angle of 0° and a distance of roughly 3 in., or 10 cm, might be reasonable, depending on your screen size.) Drag vertices of your original triangle and observe its translated image, △*A'B'C'*.

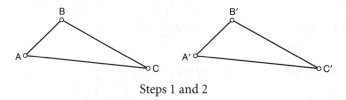

Steps 1 and 2

Step 3 Now you will dilate your second triangle so you can scale it to different sizes. First, make a changeable ratio of dilation. Construct two horizontal segments *m* and *n*. Make *n* longer than *m*.

Step 4 Select segment *m*, then *n*, and choose **Transform | Mark Segment Ratio.** Select the segments again, in the same order, and choose **Measure | Ratio.**

Step 5 Double-click *A'* in the second triangle to mark it as a center.

Step 6 Select points *B'* and *C'* and dilate them by the marked ratio. These new points, *B''* and *C''*, are new vertices of your second triangle.

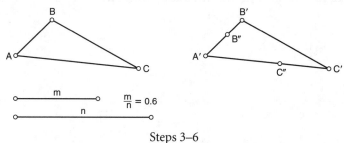

Steps 3–6

(continued)

Step 7 To finish constructing triangle $A'B''C''$, hide all parts of triangle $A'B'C'$ except point A' and construct the missing segments of the new triangle. Change your ratio and observe the results.

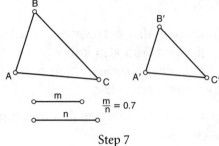

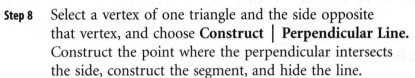

$\frac{m}{n} = 0.7$

Step 7

In Steps 8–10, you'll construct altitudes in the similar triangles and measure their ratio.

Step 8 Select a vertex of one triangle and the side opposite that vertex, and choose **Construct | Perpendicular Line.** Construct the point where the perpendicular intersects the side, construct the segment, and hide the line.

Step 9 Do the same in the other triangle.

Step 10 To measure the ratio between the altitudes, select the shorter altitude, then the longer altitude, and choose **Measure | Ratio.**

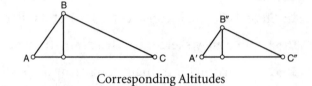

Corresponding Altitudes

Investigate

1. Drag parts of your sketch and observe the ratio of the altitudes. Record your observations.

Sketch

In Steps 11 and 12, you'll construct medians in your triangles and measure their ratio.

Step 11 Delete or hide the altitudes, and construct a pair of corresponding medians.

Step 12 Measure the ratio of the medians. (For consistency, select the median on $\triangle A'B''C''$ first.)

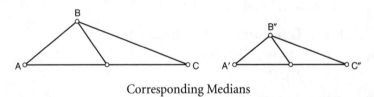

Corresponding Medians

Investigate

2. Drag parts of your sketch and observe the ratio of the medians. Record your observations.

(continued)

Lesson 11.4 • Corresponding Parts of Similar Triangles (continued)

Sketch

In Steps 13 and 14, you'll construct angle bisectors and measure their ratio.

Step 13 Delete or hide the medians, and construct a pair of corresponding angle bisectors. (To construct an angle bisector, select three points on the angle, with the vertex in the middle. Choose **Construct | Angle Bisector.** This gives you a ray. Construct the point where the ray intersects the opposite side, construct a segment, and hide the ray.)

Step 14 Measure the ratio of the angle bisectors. (For consistency, select the shorter one first.)

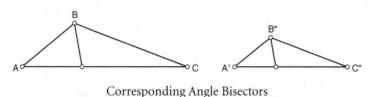

Corresponding Angle Bisectors

Investigate

3. Drag parts of your sketch and observe the ratio of the angle bisectors. Record your observations.

4. Combine your observations about altitudes, medians, and angle bisectors into a single conjecture (Proportional Parts Conjecture).

Investigation 2: Opposite Side Ratios

Sketch

Step 1 In a new sketch, use the **Ray** tool to construct an angle *BAC.*

Step 2 Bisect the angle by selecting points *B, A,* and *C* in that order, then choosing **Construct | Angle Bisector.**

Step 3 Construct a point *D* on the angle bisector and use the **Line** tool to draw a line through segment *DB.* Construct the intersection *E* of that line and the other side of the angle.

Step 4 Construct segments *ED, DB, BA,* and *AE.* Hide the line and the rays of the original angle.

Step 5 Select all segments and measure their lengths.

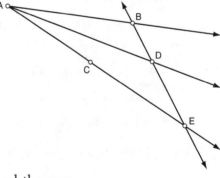

Investigate

1. Drag point *B* and look for patterns. Try calculating some ratios of segment lengths. Write the Angle Bisector/Opposite Side Conjecture to summarize your findings.

Lesson 11.5 • Area Ratios   **Demonstration**

Elias is building his dream house. He has decided to double the length and the width of the master bathroom from its dimensions in the original plans. Does that mean he should buy twice as much floor tile? In this demonstration you'll investigate how the ratio of the areas of similar figures compares to the ratio of corresponding lengths.

Sketch

Step 1 Open the sketch **Area Ratio Demo.gsp.**

Step 2 The lighter polygon is the image of the darker polygon dilated by a scale factor defined by the two horizontal segments. Drag different vertices of the two polygons to confirm that the polygons are always similar.

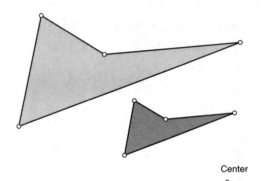

Center

Step 3 Change the scale factor by pressing *Animate* or any of the buttons with numbers on them, or by dragging point *drag*. Watch the effect different scale factors have on the area ratio and on the plot.

Investigate

1. How can you tell from their appearance that the two polygons are similar?

2. The side lengths ratio displayed in the sketch is the ratio of (choose A or B)

   A. the dark polygon's side lengths to the light polygon's side lengths.

   B. the light polygon's side lengths to the dark polygon's side lengths.

3. Copy and complete the table below. Write the area ratios as fractions.

Side lengths ratio	$\frac{1}{2}$	1	$\frac{3}{2}$	2	$\frac{5}{2}$	3
Area ratio						

4. Explain what the plot represents.

5. How should you advise Elias?

Discovering Geometry with The Geometer's Sketchpad
©2008 Key Curriculum Press

Lesson 11.5 • Proportions with Area

If two figures are similar, one is a scaled version of another, perhaps with a reflection. How are the areas of similar figures related?

Investigation: Area Ratios

Sketch

Step 1 In a new sketch, construct segments AB and CD, where $\overline{AB}$ is longer than $\overline{CD}$.

Step 2 Select $\overline{AB}$ and $\overline{CD}$ and mark $\frac{AB}{CD}$ as a ratio using the Transform menu. Select the segments again and measure their ratio. This ratio will be the scale factor for your similar polygons.

Step 3 Construct any polygon and its interior.

Step 4 Construct a point outside the polygon and double-click the point with the **Arrow** tool to mark it as a center.

Step 5 To make a second polygon similar to the first, select the sides, vertices, and interior of the first polygon, and dilate the polygon by the marked ratio. With $\overline{AB}$ longer than $\overline{CD}$, the image polygon will be bigger than the original polygon. Drag point B and experiment with changing the scale factor. Also experiment with dragging the center point.

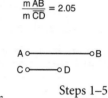

$$\frac{m\,\overline{AB}}{m\,\overline{CD}} = 2.05$$

○ Center

A ○————○ B
C ○———○ D

Steps 1–5

Step 6 Select a side of the dilated polygon, then the corresponding side of the original polygon, and measure their ratio.

Step 7 Repeat Step 6 using a different pair of corresponding sides. What is this ratio?

Step 8 Now compare the areas of the polygons in the same way. Take a minute to predict this ratio before you calculate it. Then measure the areas of both polygons. Use the calculator to find the ratio of the area of the dilated polygon to the area of the original. Did you get the ratio you predicted?

Step 9 Next, create a plot of the ratio of side lengths against the ratio of areas for different scale factors. To do this, select the measure of the ratio of the side lengths, then the calculation of the ratio of the areas. Choose **Graph | Plot As (x, y)**, then choose **Display | Trace Point.**

Step 10 Drag point B to experiment with different scale factors. The point you plotted will trace out a plot of the side-length ratio against the area ratio for different pairs of similar figures.

(continued)

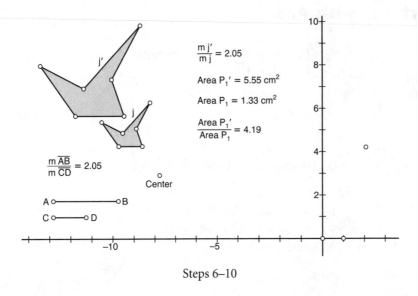

Steps 6–10

Investigate

1. Drag B so that the ratio of the side lengths is $\frac{2}{1}$, or 2. Use this information to complete the first column in a table like this one. Then complete the rest of the table. The last column uses variables so that you can generalize for any scale factor $\frac{m}{n}$.

Ratio of corresponding side lengths	2	3	1	$\frac{1}{2}$	$\frac{1}{10}$	$\frac{m}{n}$
Ratio of areas						

2. Summarize the relationship between ratios of side lengths and ratios of areas in similar figures as the Proportional Areas Conjecture.

3. Explain how the shape of the plot you created in Step 9 supports the Proportional Areas Conjecture.

Explore More

1. If your polygon is one that tessellates, explain the Proportional Areas Conjecture in terms of fitting one polygon into another. If your polygon doesn't tessellate, experiment with one that does, such as a triangle or a parallelogram.

2. Now you can compare similar shapes in three dimensions. How does the ratio of the volumes of similar solids compare to the ratio of the sides?

   a. One way to investigate this is by calculating the volumes of two cubes. Make one cube twice as long, twice as wide, and twice as tall as the other. Make sketches on paper of a pair of such cubes and show your measurements. How do the volumes compare?

   b. Compare more similar solids if necessary. Then summarize your conclusions as the Proportional Volumes Conjecture.

Lesson 11.7 • Proportional Segments Between Parallel Lines

In this activity you will cut two sides of a triangle with a segment. Then you will investigate measurements of the new pieces in the construction.

Investigation 1: Parallels and Proportionality

Sketch

Step 1 In a new sketch, construct any triangle *ABC*.

Step 2 Construct segment *DE* connecting sides *AB* and *BC*.

Step 3 Hide sides *AB* and *BC*.

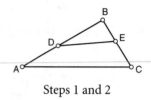

Steps 1 and 2

Step 4 Construct segments *AD*, *DB*, *BE*, and *EC*.

Step 5 Select segments *DE* and *AC* and find their slope using the Measure menu.

Step 6 Select segment *AD*, then segment *DB*, and find their ratio using the Measure menu.

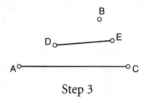

Step 3

Step 7 Select segment *CE*, then segment *EB*, and find their ratio.

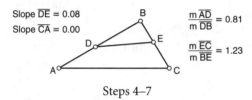

Slope $\overline{DE}$ = 0.08
Slope $\overline{CA}$ = 0.00

$\dfrac{m\,\overline{AD}}{m\,\overline{DB}}$ = 0.81

$\dfrac{m\,\overline{EC}}{m\,\overline{BE}}$ = 1.23

Steps 4–7

Investigate

1. Drag point *E* until the slopes are as equal as possible. When the slopes are equal, $\overline{DE}$ is parallel to $\overline{AC}$. What can you say about △*ABC* and △*DBE*? Explain.

2. When $\overline{DE}$ is parallel to $\overline{AC}$, what do you observe about the ratios?

3. Now investigate the converse of your observation in Question 2: Drag a vertex to change the triangle, and drag point *E* until $\overline{DE}$ is no longer parallel to $\overline{AC}$. Watching the ratios, drag point *D* or *E* until $\overline{DE}$ divides the sides proportionally. What can you say about segments *DE* and *AC*?

4. Combine your observations into a single conjecture (Parallel/Proportionality Conjecture).

(continued)

Investigation 2: Extended Parallel/Proportionality

Sketch

Step 1   In a new sketch, construct a triangle.

Step 2   Construct two points on the same side of the triangle.

Step 3   Select both points and another side of the triangle, then choose **Construct | Parallel Line.**

Step 4   Construct the two points where the parallel lines intersect the third side.

Step 5   Hide everything in your sketch except the points and the segment without any points on it.

Step 6   Connect nearby points with segments so your sketch looks like this one. (The labels may be different.)

Step 7   Measure ratios of corresponding pairs of segments. For example, compare $\frac{u}{r}$ and $\frac{v}{t}$. Also compare $\frac{u}{o}$ and $\frac{v}{q}$. Measure three such pairs of ratios.

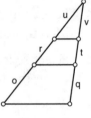

Steps 1–6

Investigate

1. Drag vertices of your original triangle and points on the edges. Observe the corresponding ratios. Summarize your observations as the Extended Parallel/Proportionality Conjecture.

EXPLORE MORE

If the three sides of one triangle are parallel to the three sides of another triangle, what do you think is true about the two triangles? Make a conjecture. Then make a construction to check your conjecture.

Lesson 12.1 • Trigonometric Ratios

In Chapter 9 of your book, you used the Pythagorean Theorem—
a powerful problem-solving tool—to find missing side lengths in right
triangles. In Chapter 11, you used proportions in similar triangles to solve
problems and to measure heights and distances indirectly. Right triangle
trigonometry builds on similar-triangle concepts to give you more ways
to find unknown measurements in triangles. In this lesson you'll learn
about trigonometric ratios and how you can use them.

Investigation: Trigonometric Tables

Sketch

Step 1 In a new sketch, construct $\overline{AB}$.

Step 2 Construct a line through point B perpendicular to $\overline{AB}$.

Step 3 Construct $\overline{AC}$, where point C is a point on the
perpendicular line.

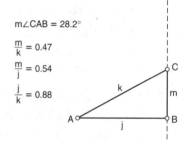

$m\angle CAB = 28.2°$

$\dfrac{m}{k} = 0.47$

$\dfrac{m}{j} = 0.54$

$\dfrac{j}{k} = 0.88$

Step 4 Hide the line.

Step 5 Construct $\overline{BC}$ to finish the right triangle.

Step 6 Show the three segments' labels, and, if necessary, change the
labels to match the labels in the figure. (To show a label, click
the segment once with the **Text** tool. Double-click the label to
change it.)

Step 7 Measure $\angle CAB$.

Step 8 Measure the ratios $\dfrac{m}{j}$, $\dfrac{m}{k}$, and $\dfrac{j}{k}$. (To measure a ratio, select two
segments in order, first the numerator, then the denominator.)

Investigate

1. Drag point C. When the angles change, do the ratios also change?

2. Drag point A or B. What do you notice about the ratios when the
angles don't change? Explain why you think this happens.

Your observations in Question 2 give you a very useful fact about right
triangles. For any right triangle with a given acute angle, each ratio of side
lengths has a given value, regardless of the size of the triangle. The three
ratios you measured are called the **tangent, sine,** and **cosine** of angle A.
Here they are defined for acute angle A.

$$\text{tangent } \angle A = \frac{\text{length of leg opposite } \angle A}{\text{length of leg adjacent to } \angle A}$$

$$\text{sine } \angle A = \frac{\text{length of leg opposite } \angle A}{\text{length of hypotenuse}}$$

$$\text{cosine } \angle A = \frac{\text{length of leg adjacent to } \angle A}{\text{length of hypotenuse}}$$

(continued)

3. Practice identifying sides by copying and completing the sine and cosine ratios for acute angle A in $\triangle ABC$.

$$\tan A = \frac{m}{j} \qquad \sin A = \frac{\square}{\square} \qquad \cos A = \frac{\square}{\square}$$

4. Drag point C so that $\angle CAB$ measures as close to 30° as you can get it. On your paper, write down approximate values for the tangent, sine, and cosine of 30°. Use the definitions given and refer to the calculations in your sketch to find these values.

5. Tangent, sine, and cosine functions can be found on all scientific calculators. Use Sketchpad's calculator to check your answers to Question 4. Make sure $m\angle CAB$ is still 30°. Open the calculator from the Measure menu; then press and hold the Functions pop-up submenu. Choose **tan,** click in the sketch on the measurement of $\angle CAB$, then click OK. Use the same process to calculate the sine and cosine of $\angle CAB$. How do these three calculations compare to the ratios in your sketch?

6. Without measuring, figure out the measure of $\angle C$ and write it down. Use Sketchpad's calculator (or a pocket calculator) to find the sine of $\angle C$. The sine of $\angle C$ should be close to one of the trigonometric ratios for $\angle CAB$. Which one? Explain why this is so.

Before electronic calculators existed, people used tables to find trigonometric ratios. By making such a table in Sketchpad, you can get a sense of some of the patterns in the trigonometric ratios.

Sketch

Step 9 Drag point C so that $m\angle CAB = 0°$ (or close to it).

Step 10 Select these measurements or calculations in order: $m\angle CAB$, $\tan(m\angle CAB)$, $\sin(m\angle CAB)$, and $\cos(m\angle CAB)$.

Step 11 Choose **Graph | Tabulate.** Double-click the table to add the first entry.

Step 12 Drag point C to make $m\angle CAB = 10°$.

Step 13 Double-click the table to add an entry.

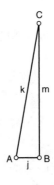

(continued)

Step 14 Continue this process to make a table for angles in 10° increments from 0° to almost 90°. You'll find that to make larger angles, you have to make $\overline{AB}$ shorter.

$m\angle CAB$	$\tan(m\angle CAB)$	$\sin(m\angle CAB)$	$\cos(m\angle CAB)$
0.2°	0.00	0.00	1.00
10.2°	0.18	0.18	0.98
20.0°	0.36	0.34	0.94
29.9°	0.57	0.50	0.87
39.9°	0.84	0.64	0.77
49.9°	1.19	0.77	0.64
60.0°	1.73	0.87	0.50
70.0°	2.75	0.94	0.34
80.0°	5.68	0.98	0.17

Investigate

7. Why couldn't you make $m\angle CAB$ exactly equal to 90°?

8. What happens to $\tan(m\angle CAB)$ as $m\angle CAB$ gets closer to 90°? What happens to $\sin(m\angle CAB)$ and $\cos(m\angle CAB)$?

9. What is the greatest possible value for the sine of an angle? What angle has this value?

10. What is the least possible value for the sine of an angle? What angle has this value?

11. For what angle (not in your table) is the tangent equal to 1? Why?

12. For what angle are the sine and cosine equal? Why?

13. Suppose an angle has measure x. Complete this equation:
$\sin x = \cos(\underline{\hspace{1cm}})$.

Lesson 12.3 • The Law of Sines

You saw in Lesson 12.1 how you can use trigonometric ratios to find unknown measurements in a right triangle. In Chapter 4, you discovered that just a few parts (for example, ASA) determine a triangle. Is it possible to find unknown measurements in *any* triangle if you know the right combination of measurements? In this lesson you'll discover a way to use the sine of an angle to find the area of a triangle. Then you'll derive a formula you can use to find all the measurements in a triangle if you know the right combination of parts.

Investigation: Area of a Triangle and the Law of Sines

Sketch

Step 1 In a new sketch, construct $\triangle ABC$. (It should not be a right triangle.)

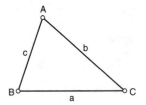

a = 2.928 cm
b = 2.977 cm
c = 2.053 cm

m∠ACB = 70.94°
sin(m∠ACB) = 0.945

Step 2 Use the **Text** tool to display the segment labels; then change each label so that the side opposite $\angle A$ is labeled *a*, and so on.

Step 3 Measure the lengths of the three sides, and measure $\angle ACB$.

Step 4 Use the calculator to calculate $\sin(m\angle ACB)$. (The sine function is in the Functions pop-up submenu of the calculator.)

Investigate

1. In your sketch, you haven't constructed or measured the height of the triangle, but you can calculate the area of the triangle without knowing the height if you use trigonometry. Start by figuring out an expression that gives the height of the triangle in terms of sin *A* and one or more of the side lengths you measured. (Draw the height in your triangle if that helps you see how it's related to the angle and the side lengths.) Write down that expression: $h = $ _____.

2. Now use the calculator to evaluate an expression that gives the area of the triangle. Test your expression by constructing the triangle interior and measuring the area. Write a conjecture stating your formula for the area of a triangle in terms of side lengths and an angle (SAS Triangle Area Conjecture).

3. Use what you've discovered to explain why these expressions are all equal.

$$\frac{1}{2}bc \sin A = \frac{1}{2}ac \sin B = \frac{1}{2}ab \sin C$$

4. It would be handy if the expressions in Question 3 each had only the angle and the side opposite the angle. Multiply and divide until you're left with expressions of that form. The simplified equation you're left with is the Law of Sines. Write down the Law of Sines.

Lesson 12.4 • Deriving the Law of Cosines   Demonstration

With the Pythagorean Theorem you can calculate one side length of a right triangle using the lengths of the other two. With the Law of Cosines you can make the same kind of calculation for all triangles. It depends on the angle.

Sketch

Step 1   Open the sketch **Law of Cosines Demo.gsp.**

Step 2   Drag the triangle's vertices and watch how the measurements change.

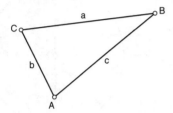

Investigate

1. Predict an expression for c^2 in terms of a^2, b^2, and angle C.

2. Be sure the angles A and B are acute and show the altitude. Can you verify the expression you predicted?

3. Follow the steps of the derivation. At each step, try to follow the instruction before pressing the button. Justify the result displayed after you press each button.

Exploration • The Unit Circle   Demonstration

In Lesson 12.1, you defined trigonometric ratios in terms of right triangles, which limited the definitions to only acute angles. In this demonstration you will use the **unit circle**—the circle in the coordinate plane with center (0, 0) and radius 1 unit—to define trigonometric ratios for more angles.

Sketch

Step 1   Open the sketch **Unit Circle Demo.gsp.**

Step 2   Using the yellow triangle and your usual definitions of the trigonometric ratios, write down ratios for the sine, cosine, and tangent of $\angle DAC$ (therefore, also of $\angle BAC$).

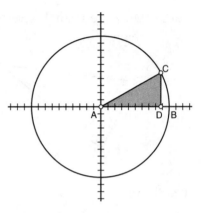

Investigate

1. What segment always has the same length as you drag C? What is that length?

2. The trigonometric ratios you wrote down are already shown in the sketch. Which one is which? Explain.

3. Drag point C around the circle and observe $m\angle BAC$ and the sine of $\angle BAC$. What is the maximum value of the sine? The minimum? For what values of $m\angle BAC$ do the maximum and minimum occur?

4. Press *Animate Points*. Point G appears and moves to the right on the x-axis at the same rate that C moves counterclockwise along the circle. Therefore, the point *sin* traces out the sine curve. How does the sine curve reflect your observations from Question 4?

5. Press *Show Tangent* and drag point C to the first quadrant somewhere. Explain why $y_E = \tan \angle BAC$.

6. Drag point C around the circle and observe $m\angle BAC$ and the tangent of $\angle BAC$. Does tangent have a maximum value? A minimum?

7. What happens to the tangent of $\angle BAC$ as $m\angle BAC$ approaches 90° or −90°? Based on the definition of tangent and the side lengths in $\triangle DAC$ (or $\triangle BAE$), what can you say about the value of the tangent of 90°?

8. Press *Animate Points* to see point *tan* trace out the tangent curve. How does the sine curve reflect your observations from Question 8?

9. Press *Show Both* and then *Animate Points* to see both curves together. Both curves end at point F, whose coordinates are given. What is the significance of the coordinates of F in terms of the unit circle? (You may wish to re-read Question 4 to remind yourself how the curves are drawn.)

10. If C continued to move along the circle and G continued to move to the right on the x-axis, how would the sine and tangent curves continue? (Curves of this nature are called **periodic.**)

Discovering Geometry with The Geometer's Sketchpad
©2008 Key Curriculum Press

Exploration • Hyperbolic Geometry **Extension**

In Chapter 13, you learned that when Euclid built his deductive system of geometry theorems in his book *The Elements*, he started with a set of postulates that he considered self-evident. He used them to prove theorems, used those theorems to prove more theorems, and so on. The conjectures you've made are based on Euclid's geometry. Somehow, though, Euclid's fifth postulate seems less self-evident than the others. It states,

> If two straight lines lying in a plane are met by another line and if the sum of the interior angles on one side is less than two right angles, then the straight lines, if extended sufficiently, will meet on the side on which the sum of the angles is less than two right angles.

A simpler, logically equivalent statement called Playfair's axiom states, "Through a point not on a given line there passes one and only one line that never meets the given line." Before you read further, make a quick sketch on a piece of paper to see if you agree with this axiom.

Mathematicians long sought to prove the postulate, however it was stated, using Euclid's other four postulates, or to replace it with something more self-evident. In the early 19th century, mathematicians discovered that if you assume the postulate is not true, you can build new deductive systems of geometry in which some theorems from Euclidean geometry remain the same and some are quite different. These non-Euclidean geometries typically replace Euclid's fifth postulate with one of these assumptions:

Assumption 1   Through a given point not on a given line there pass more than one line parallel to the given line.

Assumption 2   Through a given point not on a given line there pass no lines parallel to the given line.

You might have experimented with elliptic geometry, in which the second assumption is true. In this activity you'll use The Geometer's Sketchpad to explore a geometry, called hyperbolic geometry, based on one of these assumptions (you will figure out which assumption). One model of this geometry takes place within a disk, called the **Poincaré disk,** devised by French mathematician Henri Poincaré (1854–1912).

Investigation: The Poincaré Disk

Step 1   Open the sketch **Poincare Disk.gsp.**

Step 2   Check the Custom Tools menu to see a list of nine custom tools that accompany this sketch. The only tools you should use are these **Custom** tools and Sketchpad's **Selection Arrow** and **Point** tools. Don't use any other tools, and don't use the Construct, Transform, Measure, or Graph menus. Whenever you're asked to construct a line, segment, or circle, use the Poincaré custom tools to construct these objects.

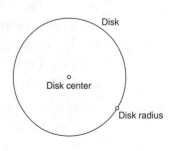

(continued)

Step 3 Play with the **Custom** tools to get a feel for what they do. Use them to construct hyperbolic segments, lines, and circles, and drag the figures around with the **Selection Arrow** tool. Everything you construct should be inside the disk. If you construct or drag anything outside the disk, don't expect the rules of Poincaré geometry to apply. Measure distances and angles using the Custom Tools menu. Write down four or five observations you make about this geometry.

Step 4 Now it's time to explore Poincaré geometry more systematically. Go to page 2 in the sketch, and construct a hyperbolic line. Describe the line and how it meets the edge of the disk. (You may find that when you drag lines so that they pass through the center, they disappear momentarily. This is not a property of Poincaré geometry; it is just a limitation of the custom tool.)

Step 5 Use the regular **Point** tool to construct a point inside the disk but not on the hyperbolic line. How many hyperbolic lines can be drawn through the point that don't intersect the given hyperbolic line? Which of the two assumptions in the introduction is Poincaré geometry based on?

Step 6 In the Poincaré disk, distances are defined quite differently. Use the **Hyperbolic Circle by CR** custom tool to construct a hyperbolic circle somewhere inside the disk (CR stands for Center+Radius). You will have to click three times in the disk for the circle to appear. The first click gives you the center of the circle, and the second and third clicks define the radius. Use a custom tool to measure the hyperbolic distance between the two radius endpoints and between the center and a point on the hyperbolic circle. Drag the point around the hyperbolic circle. Drag the center of the hyperbolic circle. Do your observations affirm that on a hyperbolic circle all points are equidistant from the center? But it doesn't look that way, does it? Which radii look shorter to your Euclidean eye: radii that go toward the center of the disk or radii that go toward the edge of the disk?

Step 7 Now it's time for a non-Euclidean conjecture. Go to page 3 in the sketch, and construct a hyperbolic triangle. Use the **Hyperbolic Angle** custom tool to measure the three angles, and use the calculator to sum them. Drag the vertices of the triangle. You should observe that the angle sum, unlike that in a Euclidean triangle, is not a constant. What range can this sum have? Write a conjecture.

Step 8 Investigate the Isosceles Triangle Conjecture in the Poincaré disk. To construct an isosceles triangle, construct a hyperbolic circle and

(continued)

two radii; then connect the radius endpoints for the third side of your triangle. Remember that hyperbolic distances appear distorted, so your triangle may not look isosceles. Use the **Hyperbolic Distance** custom tool to confirm that it is. Then measure angles and make a conjecture about base angles in a hyperbolic isosceles triangle.

Step 9   Devise and perform an investigation of your own on the Poincaré disk. Describe what you did and what you discovered.

CHAPTER 0

LESSON 0.2 · Line Designs   EXT

EXAMPLE SKETCH

Line Design.gsp

LESSON GUIDE

In Lesson 0.2 of the student book, students see more
than just this type of line design, and they get practice
using a straightedge to make careful drawings. You
might have the class do the lesson in the book and
save this extension for later in the year.

SKETCH

Step 1: Choose **Preferences** from the Edit menu. In the
Text panel, check Show Labels Automatically For All
New Points.

Step 11: To avoid errant segments, have students
select the two points they want to connect, then
choose **Segment** from the Construct menu.

Step 12: Highlight the **Point** tool and choose **Select All
Points** from the Edit menu. Holding down the Shift key,
click on points *A, B,* and *C* to deselect them before you
choose **Hide Points** from the Display menu.

Step 14: Highlight the **Segment** tool and choose **Select
All Segments** from the Edit menu.

INVESTIGATE

1. $\overleftrightarrow{AB}$

2. a. $\overleftrightarrow{AB}$ and $\overleftrightarrow{AC}$

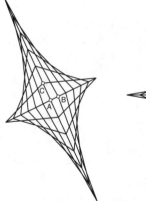

b. $\overleftrightarrow{AB}$, $\overleftrightarrow{AC}$, and two more
   at 45° angles to those

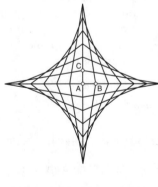

c. One through each corner, passing through the
   center (This figure is hard to make—two sets
   of segments overlap to reduce the four sets
   to three.)

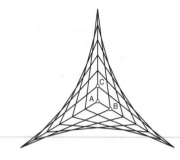

EXPLORE MORE

Students can create dynamic versions of the examples in
Lesson 0.2 of the student book.

LESSON 0.3 · Circle Designs   EXT

EXAMPLE SKETCH

Hex Designs.gsp

LESSON GUIDE

In Lesson 0.3 in the student book, students get practice
using a compass, so don't use this extension as a replacement. Instead, you might save it for later in the year.

SKETCH

Step 2: Make sure students use points *B* and *A* to define
the second circle. Some may use *B* for the center of a
circle that merely passes through *A* but whose radius is
defined by a third point. That will cause their designs to
fall apart if dragged.

Step 5: Sketchpad will not allow the construction of an
intersection of three objects, as such an intersection is
not usually defined by a single point. To construct an
intersection of three objects, you must select two of
them and use the Construct menu.

Step 6: Point out that by using the **Segment** tool to
connect the outside points of the daisy, students can
construct a regular hexagon. They can construct a
6-point star by connecting alternate points to create
intersecting equilateral triangles. Midpoints can be useful
in creating more complex designs. Encourage students to
experiment and practice using different tools.

INVESTIGATE

Designs will vary.

EXAMPLE SKETCH

Rosettes.gsp

LESSON GUIDE

Students use Sketchpad to create a Roman rosette, a design based on the daisy. Students can also create rosettes with a compass and straightedge, but they would need to work quite carefully, as the design is quite detailed. You can use this extension any time after Lesson 0.3.

SKETCH

Step 1: Students can follow the directions for the Circle Designs extension, Steps 1–5, if they have not previously used Sketchpad to make a daisy design. The design will be cleaner if only the control point has a label.

Step 2: Allow students to experiment with ways to place a point midway between two points on the circle. If you use this activity later in the year, students may construct an angle bisector or, using the center of the original circle as a center of rotation, choose **Transform | Rotate** to rotate each of the six original points 30° around the circle. However, the most intuitive method is to construct a segment from the center point to the intersection of two of the outer circles. This segment will bisect the arc between two points.

INVESTIGATE

Sample design:

LESSON 0.4 • Op Art   EXT

EXAMPLE SKETCH AND TOOL

Tumbling Blocks.gsp and **6/Hexagon (Inscribed)** in **Polygons.gsp**

LESSON GUIDE

This lesson can replace Lesson 0.4 in the student book, though some familiarity with Sketchpad would be very useful. Don't make this your students' introduction to Sketchpad. You could make this activity an extension for students who show particular interest in working on computers, or you could save it for later in the school year. You might assign this extension when students study tessellations in Chapter 7.

SKETCH

Step 1: The hexagon tool is available in the sketch **Polygons.gsp**, located in the **Custom Tools** folder on the CD.

Step 4: The segments and polygon interiors constructed in this step divide the hexagon into three congruent rhombuses.

Step 5: Student labels are unlikely to match the figure. Students need to select appropriate points to translate the figure horizontally by the width of the block.

Step 6: **Select All** is in the Edit menu when the **Arrow** tool is chosen in the Toolbox. Make sure By Marked Vector is checked in the Translate dialog box.

Step 7: As long as you don't click anywhere, the translated figure from the previous step will be selected, ready to translate again.

Step 12: Choose the **Point** tool and choose **Edit | Select All Points.** While all the points are selected, choose the **Arrow** tool and click on *A* and *B* to deselect them. Hide the remaining selected points.

INVESTIGATE

1. The tumbling block design is composed of regular hexagons divided into rhombuses. Point out to students that this is an example of a *tessellation*—a tiling of the plane without gaps or overlap.

2. The blocks tend to pop in and out. One moment you see blocks coming out of the page, and another moment it may appear as if you're looking up from beneath and new blocks appear, with the old blocks turning inside out.

EXPLORE MORE

Answers will vary.

LESSON 0.6 • Islamic Tile Designs   EXT

EXAMPLE SKETCH AND TOOL

Islamic Design.gsp and **4/Square (Inscribed)** in **Polygons.gsp**

LESSON GUIDE

This lesson can replace Lesson 0.6 in the student book, though some previous familiarity with Sketchpad would be useful. Don't make this students' introduction to

Sketchpad. You could make this activity an optional approach for students who show particular interest in working on computers, or you could save it for later in the school year.

SKETCH

Step 1: Students need not use a **Custom** tool to construct a square, but one way or another they need to start with a square. The square tool is available in the sketch **Polygons.gsp** in the **Custom Tools** folder on the CD.

Step 5: Click on the intersection with the **Point** tool or the **Arrow** tool.

Step 8: There are other ways to draw the knot design that some students might find easier than the one described here. Encourage those who have trouble following Step 8 to try their own methods.

Step 10: To construct a polygon interior, select the points at the vertices of the region and choose **Construct | Polygon Interior.** With a hint, some students might notice that they need only construct two polygon interiors of contrasting colors, which can then be rotated 90° to color the rest of the knot.

Step 14: The easiest way to hide a lot of points is to select the **Point** tool, choose **Edit | Select All Points,** click on the points you don't want to hide to deselect them, then choose **Display | Hide Points.**

EXPLORE MORE

Refer students to the Hexagon Tile Design on page 21 of the student book for an example of a hexagon-based design.

CHAPTER 1

USING YOUR ALGEBRA SKILLS 1 · Midpoint

EXAMPLE SKETCH

Midpoint.gsp

LESSON GUIDE

Use this activity as a replacement for, or a review of, Using Your Algebra Skills 1.

SKETCH

Step 4: If students select all three points first, they can measure all three coordinates at the same time.

INVESTIGATE

1. The *x*-coordinate of the midpoint is always exactly halfway between the *x*-coordinates of the endpoints. The same is true for the *y*-coordinate. You may want to encourage students to use the word *average*. Students might have trouble seeing the pattern if the coordinate values are precise to many decimal

places. To change the precision, choose **Display | Preferences.**

2. If (x_1, y_1) and (x_2, y_2) are the coordinates of the endpoints of a segment, then the coordinates of the midpoint are $\left(\frac{x_1 + x_2}{2}, \frac{y_1 + y_2}{2}\right)$ (Coordinate Midpoint Property).

3. Answers will vary. This problem gives students a chance to check their conjecture on numbers that are not integers. The conjecture holds for any real numbers, not just integers.

EXPLORE MORE

This problem gives students a chance to check the coordinate midpoint property. The advice in the lesson for selecting the *y*-coordinate and *x*-coordinate only is important, as this part of the construction can be confusing.

LESSON 1.5 · Triangles

REQUIRED SKETCH

Triangles.gsp

LESSON GUIDE

This activity is suitable for beginning Sketchpad users because students work with a prepared sketch. It can be used to replace the Triangles investigation in Lesson 1.5. Students need only to be able to measure angles. This lesson helps introduce students to Sketchpad constructions. For example, when novice users are asked to construct right triangles, they often draw arbitrary triangles and manipulate them until they approximate right triangles. The experience students get with this sketch should give them a sense of how to construct figures with proper constraints according to their definitions. The Explore More questions ask students to try some of these constructions themselves.

Make sure to summarize the lesson by agreeing on definitions as a class.

INVESTIGATE

1. Answers will vary, but most students will find △*ABC* to be the least constrained.

2. Answers will vary. The equilateral triangle, △*GHI*, will get many votes for most constrained.

3. Three; it will always have at least two.

4. One   **5.** △*DEF* (the isosceles triangle)

6. △*LMN*   **7.** △*GHI*   **8.** Scalene

9. △*LMN* (the right triangle)

10. △*DEF*, △*GHI* (the equilateral triangle)

11. △*GHI*

12. Possible

13. Not possible   **14.** Not possible

15. Possible   **16.** Possible

 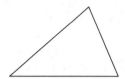

17. An acute triangle is a triangle with three acute angles.

An obtuse triangle is a triangle with one obtuse angle.

A right triangle is a triangle with one right angle.

A scalene triangle is a triangle with three sides of different lengths.

An isosceles triangle is a triangle with at least two sides the same length.

An equilateral triangle is a triangle with three sides the same length.

EXPLORE MORE

1. Answers will vary. Possible construction: Construct a segment to be one leg of the right triangle. Then construct a perpendicular line through one endpoint of the segment. To complete the triangle, construct a point on the perpendicular line and hide the perpendicular line. Construct segments to the third point.

2. Answers will vary. Possible construction for an isosceles triangle: Construct a circle *D* with control point *E*. Construct point *F* on the circle. Connect points *D, E,* and *F* with segments to form an isosceles triangle. Possible construction for an equilateral triangle: Construct segment *GH*. Construct circle *G* with radius $\overline{GH}$ and circle *H* with radius $\overline{HG}$. Construct point *I* at the intersection of the two circles. Connect points *I, G,* and *H* to form an equilateral triangle.

LESSON 1.6 • Classifying Parallelograms   DEMO

REQUIRED SKETCH

Parallelogram Demo.gsp

LESSON GUIDE

In the demonstration, students define parallelogram, rhombus, rectangle, and square, but not trapezoid, kite, or the types of triangles. You may need to review the terms *equilateral* and *equiangular* first.

INVESTIGATE

1. The most common answer is the parallelogram. It's possible to change both its angles and its side lengths by dragging any of the three points.

2. The most common answer is the square. Dragging either of the two points changes the side lengths, but the four lengths remain equal to each other. It's not possible to change the angles.

3. Some students may find the rectangle more flexible because it's possible to make the side lengths unequal. But it's not possible to change the angles. Some students may find the rhombus more flexible because it's possible to change the angles. But it's not possible to make the side lengths unequal.

4. Possible answer: Opposite sides are parallel and congruent.

5. Parallelogram, rectangle (If students get the message "Nothing will move now . . . ," they should ignore it and click OK.)

6. Rhombus, square   **7.** Rhombus

8. Square   **9.** Parallelogram, rhombus

10. Rectangle, square   **11.** Rectangle

12. Square   **13.** Square

14. A parallelogram is a quadrilateral with two pairs of parallel sides.

15. A rhombus is an equilateral parallelogram.

16. A rectangle is an equiangular parallelogram.

17. A square is an equilateral and equiangular parallelogram (or an equilateral rectangle, or an equiangular rhombus, or a rectangular rhombus).

18. Sometimes. It is a rhombus when it is equilateral, in which case it is also a square.

19. Always. It is an equiangular quadrilateral.

20. Sometimes. It is a square when it is equilateral and equiangular.

21. (Rhombuses and rectangles can be interchanged.)

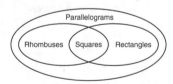

Lesson 1.6 • Special Quadrilaterals

REQUIRED SKETCH

Special Quadrilaterals.gsp

LESSON GUIDE

This activity can be used to replace the Special Quadrilaterals Investigation of Lesson 1.6. Investigation 1 concerns trapezoids and kites, and Investigation 2 covers squares, rhombuses, parallelograms, and rectangles. Students need only to be able to measure angles, lengths, and slopes.

Note that in the student book students define *trapezoid* and *kite* exclusively. That is, a trapezoid cannot be a parallelogram and a kite cannot be a rhombus. Exclusive definitions of *trapezoid* and *kite* are standard in most books, yet a Sketchpad trapezoid can be manipulated into a parallelogram, and a Sketchpad kite can be manipulated into a rhombus. Questions 2 and 4 in Investigation 3 address those restrictions to the definitions of *trapezoid* and *kite*. On the other hand, parallelogram definitions are inclusive. That is, a square is a rhombus and a rectangle, and rhombuses and rectangles are both parallelograms. These inclusive definitions are more consistent with Sketchpad constructions. For example, a construction with just the constraints of a parallelogram can be manipulated into a rhombus, a rectangle, or a square.

Be sure to summarize the lesson by agreeing on definitions as a class. Contrast the exclusive definitions of *trapezoid* and *kite* with the inclusive definitions of the different types of parallelograms.

INVESTIGATION 1

SKETCH

Step 3: To measure a slope, select a straight object (segment, ray, or line) and choose **Measure | Slope.**

INVESTIGATE

1. In general, exactly one pair of sides of the trapezoid is parallel.

2. A trapezoid is a quadrilateral with exactly one pair of parallel sides.

3. In general, a kite has two pairs of consecutive sides that are equal in length.

4. A kite is a quadrilateral with exactly two pairs of distinct congruent consecutive sides.

INVESTIGATION 2

INVESTIGATE

1. A parallelogram is a quadrilateral with two pairs of parallel opposite sides.

2. A rectangle is a quadrilateral with four congruent angles.

3. A rhombus is a quadrilateral with four congruent sides.

4. A square is a quadrilateral with four congruent sides and four congruent angles.

5. A rhombus that is also a rectangle is a square.

6. A rectangle that is also a rhombus is a square.

7. A square is an equiangular rhombus or an equilateral rectangle.

8. sometimes   9. sometimes   10. always

11. always   12. never

EXPLORE MORE

1. Constructions will vary. It is straightforward to construct a trapezoid that is sometimes a parallelogram, but more difficult to construct a trapezoid with the restriction that the legs not be parallel. Similarly, students may quickly find ways to construct a kite that is sometimes a rhombus, but not be able to construct a "robust" kite that fits the exclusive definition of the book. The learning comes from the failed attempts as much as from successful attempts, so encourage students to analyze each attempt and share their observations with other students.

2. Constructions will vary. Students may have more success with this after Chapter 3, where they do compass and straightedge constructions on paper.

Lesson 1.7 • Defining Circle Terms   DEMO

REQUIRED SKETCH

Circle Terms Demo.gsp

LESSON GUIDE

This demonstration may replace Lesson 1.7 in the student book. Students use a premade sketch to discover many of the definitions given in the lesson. If you can take students to the lab, use the activity Circles because it includes many Sketchpad skills that will be useful for later activities.

INVESTIGATE

1. Possible answers: A radius of a circle is a segment with one endpoint on the circle and the other at the center of the circle. A chord is a segment with both endpoints on a circle. A diameter is a chord that passes through the center of the circle. A tangent is a line that intersects a circle in exactly one point. A secant is a line that intersects a circle in two points.

2. A diameter is a special kind of chord. Students might draw a Venn diagram that shows diameters as a subset of chords.

3. Yes, two circles can be tangent to the same line at the same point. Students might add examples to the sketch. Two possibilities are shown:

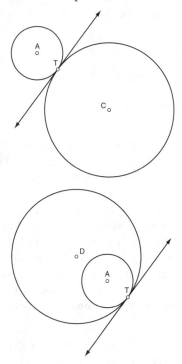

4. If there are two circles with the same center, it is clearer to name them with two letters.

5. Possible answers: Concentric circles are circles that share the same center. Congruent circles are circles with congruent radii.

6. $\overline{EB}$ is a diameter of circle A because it passes through the center.

7. Possible answers: A semicircle is an arc whose endpoints are endpoints of a diameter of a circle. A minor arc of a circle is an arc that is smaller than a semicircle. A major arc of a circle is an arc that is larger than a semicircle. Semicircles and major arcs are named with three letters to avoid confusing them with the arc with the same endpoints that completes the full circle.

8. Possible answer: A central angle in a circle is an angle with its vertex at the center of the circle. The measure of a minor arc is equal to the measure of the central angle that passes through its endpoints. The measure of a major arc is equal to 360° minus the measure of the central angle, or the reflex measure of the central angle.

LESSON 1.7 · Circles

EXAMPLE SKETCH

Circles.gsp

LESSON GUIDE

This activity replaces Lesson 1.7 in the student book. Here students discover many of the definitions given in the lesson. Students also define *secant,* which is not covered in the book. This activity introduces a number of important Sketchpad skills, so you might use it before Lesson 3.7, or before Chapter 6 as way to both review circle vocabulary and give students experience with Sketchpad.

SKETCH

Step 1: Naming circles after two points is unconventional, but it's convenient when referring to Sketchpad circles. See the answer to Question 3.

Steps 4 and 5: The order in which students select points is important in these steps! Selecting point B and then point C in Step 4 gives a different arc than selecting point C and then point B in Step 5. Sketchpad constructs an arc in counterclockwise order. Therefore, one selection order of endpoints gives the minor arc and the other selection order gives the major arc, so arc $BC \not\cong$ arc CB, as is usually the case. Explain this to students if confusion arises.

INVESTIGATE

1. AC doesn't change. A circle is defined as the set of all points in a plane at a given distance from a given point in the plane. Point C can represent any point on the circle, and AC is the given distance from the given point, point A.

2. **Distance** (select the center and a point on the circle) and **Length** (select a segment drawn from the center to a point on the circle)

3. Infinitely many circles can share the same center. Naming a circle after two points can prevent confusion when two or more circles share the same center.

4. Congruent circles are circles that have the same radius. You might point out that circle E is also controlled by radius point B, so it is not named by two points. The Construct menu command **Circle By Center+Radius** is useful in many constructions. It gives you a fixed radius compass (unlike the free-hand **Circle** tool) for duplicating lengths.

5. $\overarc{BFC}$ or $\overarc{CFB}$

6. Because two points can divide a circle into two semicircles, it's necessary to distinguish one semicircle from the other by naming them after three points. Students should add a point G to their sketches. One semicircle is $\overarc{BFC}$ or $\overarc{CFB}$ and the other is $\overarc{BGC}$ or $\overarc{CGB}$.

Discovering Geometry with The Geometer's Sketchpad

7. The measure of a minor arc is equal to the measure of the central angle that passes through its endpoints. The measure of a major arc is equal to 360° minus the measure of the central angle, or the reflex measure of the central angle.

8. A chord is a segment whose endpoints are points on a circle.

9. A diameter is a chord that passes through the center of the circle.

10. A secant is a line that intersects a circle at two points.

11. A tangent is a line that intersects a circle at exactly one point.

EXPLORE MORE

1. Possible method: Construct circle AB. Mark point A as a center for rotation and rotate point B by 180°. Construct diameter $\overline{BB'}$. This method is nice because both points B and B' are fully draggable. Another possible method: Construct a circle AB and a line AB. Construct point C where the line intersects the circle. Construct diameter CB.

It may be easiest to construct a circle given a diameter (though that wasn't the task): Construct a segment and its midpoint. Construct a circle from the midpoint to either endpoint.

2. Some students will probably notice the perpendicularity. Have them test their idea by constructing a circle and a radius segment. Through the radius endpoint on the circle, construct a line perpendicular to the radius. They will see this as a formal conjecture in Lesson 6.1.

CHAPTER 2

LESSON 2.4 · Overlapping Segments   DEMO

REQUIRED SKETCH

Overlapping Segments Demo.gsp

LESSON GUIDE

This demonstration can be used to replace the Investigation in Lesson 2.4.

INVESTIGATE

1. $\overline{AB}$, $\overline{AC}$, $\overline{AD}$, $\overline{BC}$, $\overline{BD}$, and $\overline{CD}$

2. Possible answer: it appears that $\overline{AC} \cong \overline{BD}$.

3. $\overline{AC} \cong \overline{BD}$; If $\overline{AD}$ has points A, B, C, and D in that order with $\overline{AB} \cong \overline{CD}$, then $\overline{AC} \cong \overline{BD}$.

4. AC; BD

5. $AB + BC = AC$ from Question 4, and $AB = CD$ because $\overline{AB} \cong \overline{CD}$. Therefore by substitution,

$CD + BC = AC$. The sum in this equation is equal to the sum in the second equation in Question 4, so by substitution again, $AC = BD$. Hence $\overline{AC} \cong \overline{BD}$.

LESSON 2.4 · Overlapping Angles   DEMO

REQUIRED SKETCH

Overlapping Angles Demo.gsp

LESSON GUIDE

This demonstration can replace or extend the mini-investigation of Exercise 10 in Lesson 2.4. The last two questions cover the proof of Exercise 11. You might have students work together on Question 5 after they have completed Questions 1–4. Be sure to allow time for students to discuss their proofs.

INVESTIGATE

1. $\angle APC$, $\angle APD$, $\angle APB$, $\angle CPD$, $\angle CPB$, and $\angle DPB$

2. Possible answer: it appears that $\angle APD \cong \angle CPB$.

3. $\angle APD \cong \angle CPB$; If points C and D lie in the interior of $\angle APB$, and $\angle APC \cong \angle DPB$, then $\angle APD \cong \angle CPB$.

4. $m\angle APD$; $m\angle CPB$

5. $m\angle APC + m\angle CPD = m\angle APD$ from Question 4, and $m\angle APC = m\angle DPB$ because $\angle APC \cong \angle DPB$. Therefore by substitution, $\angle DPB + m\angle CPD = m\angle APD$. The sum in this equation is equal to the sum in the second equation in Question 4, so by substitution again, $m\angle APD = m\angle CPB$. Hence $\angle APD \cong \angle CPB$.

LESSON 2.5 · Linear Pairs and Vertical Angles   DEMO

REQUIRED SKETCH

Intersecting Lines Demo.gsp

LESSON GUIDE

The two parts of this demonstration cover Investigations 1 and 2 in the student book.

INVESTIGATE

1. No (only if $\overline{SR} \perp \overline{PQ}$)

2. Yes. Their sum is always 180°.

3. Supplementary

4. If two angles form a linear pair, then they are supplementary (Linear Pair Conjecture).

5. Yes; $m\angle ACD = m\angle BCE$, $m\angle ACE = m\angle DCB$

6. Yes; the linear pairs

7. If two angles are vertical angles, then they are congruent (Vertical Angles Conjecture).

8. Explanations may vary. Because $\angle ACD$ and $\angle BCD$ form a linear pair, they are supplementary. So, $m\angle ACD + m\angle BCD = 180°$. By the same reasoning, $m\angle ECB + m\angle BCD = 180°$. By subtracting $m\angle BCD$ from both sides of each equation, $m\angle ACD$ and $m\angle ECB$ are each found to equal $180° - m\angle BCD$, so by substitution, $m\angle ACD = m\angle ECB$. Similar reasoning can be used to show that $m\angle BCD = m\angle ACE$.

LESSON 2.5 · Angle Relationships

EXAMPLE SKETCH

Angle Relationships.gsp

LESSON GUIDE

This activity covers the investigations in Lesson 2.5 in the student book, but not the example. The two investigations are combined here.

The Explore More questions are good for students who work through the activity quickly and need an extra challenge. They also review some basic algebra skills.

SKETCH

Steps 1 and 2: It's best if students construct these lines as instructed so that the lines share a control point A. This method ensures that the point of intersection A will remain fixed when students move point B or C.

INVESTIGATE

1. No matter what you drag, two pairs of angles are always congruent. Students may also notice that a pair of angles that are not congruent add to 180°.

2. a. Besides $\angle BAC$ and $\angle CAD$ already given, $\angle CAD$ and $\angle DAE$, $\angle DAE$ and $\angle EAB$, and $\angle EAB$ and $\angle BAC$ are linear pairs.

b. If two angles are a linear pair, then they are supplementary (Linear Pair Conjecture).

3. Angles in a linear pair are congruent if and only if the angles are right angles.

4. If two angles are vertical angles, then they are congruent (Vertical Angles Conjecture).

EXPLORE MORE

1. a. When three lines intersect, you can find all six angles if you know the measures of any two nonvertical angles.

b. The angles are all congruent if and only if each angle measures 60°.

2. a. When four lines intersect, you can find all eight angles if you know the measures of three angles, as long as no two of the angles are a vertical pair.

b. The angles are all congruent if and only if each angle measures 45°.

3. a. When n lines intersect, you can find all $2n$ angles if you know the measures of $n - 1$ angles, as long as no two of the angles are a vertical pair.

b. The angles are all congruent if and only if each angle measures $\frac{360°}{n}$.

LESSON 2.6 · Special Angles on Parallel Lines

EXAMPLE SKETCH

Parallel Lines.gsp

LESSON GUIDE

The activity covers the same material as the two investigations in Lesson 2.6. If you are short on time, you can use the example sketch **Parallel Lines.gsp** for a demonstration.

INVESTIGATION 1

SKETCH

Step 3: As students construct the transversal, make sure that they begin with one of the points and don't release the mouse until the other point is highlighted. This will ensure that the three lines are attached correctly.

Step 4: Make sure students locate the points as shown so that their figures correspond to the angles described later. They can use the **Text** tool to change individual point labels. You might have students save their sketches to use later for the Explore More questions.

INVESTIGATE

1. $\angle DCF$, $\angle ACE$, $\angle BAH$, and $\angle GAC$ are always congruent. $\angle DGF$, $\angle FCE$, $\angle CAB$, and $\angle GAH$ are also congruent.

2. a. Besides the sample pair $\angle FCE$ and $\angle CAB$, there are three more pairs: $\angle ECA$ and $\angle BAH$, $\angle ACD$ and $\angle HAG$, and $\angle GAC$ and $\angle DCF$.

b. If two parallel lines are cut by a transversal, then corresponding angles are congruent (Corresponding Angles, or CA, Conjecture).

3. a. Besides the sample pair $\angle ECA$ and $\angle CAG$, there is one more pair: $\angle DCA$ and $\angle CAB$.

b. If two parallel lines are cut by a transversal, then alternate interior angles are congruent (Alternate Interior Angles, or AIA, Conjecture).

4. a. Besides the sample pair $\angle FCE$ and $\angle HAG$, there is one more pair: $\angle DCF$ and $\angle BAH$.

b. If two parallel lines are cut by a transversal, then alternate exterior angles are congruent (Alternate Exterior Angles, or AEA, Conjecture).

5. If two parallel lines are cut by a transversal, then corresponding angles are congruent, alternate interior angles are congruent, and alternate exterior angles are congruent (Parallel Lines Conjecture).

6. The converse may be difficult for students to understand. This question gives students a chance to understand the converse and speculate about its truth or falsity before following a set of steps to test it on the computer.

INVESTIGATION 2

SKETCH

Steps 1 and 2: Students can construct these lines any way they want, as long as there are enough points to measure all eight angles and as long as the points of intersection are properly constructed to be on two lines simultaneously.

Step 3: It might be difficult to get the angle measurements to match exactly, especially if the measurements are very precise. To make this step easier, you could change the measurements to a rougher precision by choosing **Edit | Preferences.**

INVESTIGATE

1. If two lines are cut by a transversal to form pairs of congruent corresponding angles, congruent alternate interior angles, and congruent alternate exterior angles, then the lines are parallel (Converse of the Parallel Lines Conjecture).

EXPLORE MORE

1. There are two pairs of consecutive interior angles. Their names will vary, depending on the labels in the sketch. Sample conjecture: If parallel lines are cut by a transversal, then consecutive interior angles are supplementary.

2. There are two pairs of consecutive exterior angles. Their names will vary, depending on the labels in the sketch. Sample conjecture: If parallel lines are cut by a transversal, then consecutive exterior angles are supplementary.

3. Rotate $\overleftrightarrow{AC}$ by the marked angle to get it parallel to $\overleftrightarrow{AB}$. You can use the Converse of the Parallel Lines Conjecture to conclude that lines constructed in this manner must be parallel. Sample explanation: The construction guarantees that a pair of alternate interior angles is congruent. If one pair of alternate interior angles is congruent, you can use the Vertical Angles Conjecture and the Linear Pair Conjecture to show that each other pair of corresponding angles and every pair of alternate interior and alternate exterior angles are also congruent. Once you have shown all these pairs to be congruent, you can use the Converse of the Parallel Lines Conjecture to conclude that the lines are parallel. Clearly, every student won't go through this much deductive rigor. You can probably be satisfied if they are able to explain how they are using the converse in this construction.

USING YOUR ALGEBRA SKILLS 2 · Slope

REQUIRED SKETCH

Slope of a Line.gsp

EXAMPLE SKETCH

Slope Game.gsp

LESSON GUIDE

The three investigations in this activity could replace the information and examples in the book. Investigation 1 is a brief introduction to slope that allows students to develop or review an intuitive connection between the slope of a line and the appearance of the line. This also prepares them for Investigation 2, Playing the Slope Game, which gives them a fun way to test their knowledge of slope. Finally, Investigation 3 develops a method for calculating the slope of a line using a pair of coordinate points on the line. This leads to the slope formula.

You can pick some of these computer activities and use the student book for any missing concepts. Your students have probably studied slope in a previous class, so the work might move quickly.

INVESTIGATION 1

SKETCH

This is a very simple construction.

INVESTIGATE

1. Lines going "downhill" from left to right have negative slope. Lines going "uphill" from left to right have positive slope. The direction "from left to right" is essential.

2. Zero

3. If you ignore the sign of the slope measurement, a larger value indicates a steeper slope. This might be a good time to review absolute value, because the absolute value of the slope measurement is always larger for steeper slopes.

4. Undefined, sometimes called infinite

INVESTIGATION 2

SKETCH

You can use the example sketch **Slope Game.gsp** to replace this construction.

Step 4: It is very important that no labels are showing. To turn off a label, click the labeled object with the **Text** tool. Also, you can change which labels show up automatically by choosing **Display | Preferences.** If all points are labeled, this shortcut is effective. Choose the **Point** tool, and then choose **Display | Select All Points.** With all points selected, choose **Display | Hide Labels.**

Step 6: Students often have perfect scores, which helps build their confidence. Have students play this game for a few rounds. If you wish, have them record their scores on the board after a certain number of rounds. This is an easy way for you to check how they are doing.

INVESTIGATION 3

SKETCH

Step 2: This step may be difficult for students. Remind them that the *y*-coordinate records the vertical positioning of a point. It's important that they don't measure the vertical side of the right triangle because this measurement will not represent the change from *D* to *A* if that change is negative.

Step 4: Make sure students select the measurements themselves to put in the calculator, rather than typing in the numbers that happen to be on the screen.

INVESTIGATE

1. The ratio $\frac{rise}{run}$ remains unchanged for these triangles.

2. The ratio $\frac{rise}{run}$ is zero for a horizontal line.

3. The ratio $\frac{rise}{run}$ is undefined. The measurement may show up as the infinity symbol.

4. When the ratio $\frac{rise}{run}$ is negative, the line slopes "downhill" from left to right.

5. The slope of the line matches the ratio $\frac{rise}{run}$, so to calculate slope find the rise and run between a pair of points and calculate the ratio of these two numbers.

6. The slope *m* of a line (or segment) through $P_1\left(x_1, y_1\right)$ and $P_2\left(x_2, y_2\right)$ is $m = \frac{y_2 - y_1}{x_2 - x_1}$ where $x_1 \neq x_2$ (Slope Formula).

EXPLORE MORE

Here students check the slope formula. The calculator can be tricky to use for more complicated calculations. Students can use the Delete key to erase mistakes.

CHAPTER 3

LESSON 3.2 • Constructing Perpendicular Bisectors

EXAMPLE SKETCH

Perpendicular Bisector.gsp

LESSON GUIDE

This activity covers all the conjectures in Lesson 3.2 in the student book. However, in the exercise set, students are asked to do patty-paper and compass-and-straightedge constructions. Refer students to the investigations in their book for guidance on how to do these constructions.

INVESTIGATION 1

SKETCH

Step 3: Make sure students use points *B* and *A* for circle *BA* instead of merely constructing a circle with center *B* that happens to pass through *A* but is defined by a third point.

INVESTIGATE

1. *E* is the midpoint of $\overline{AB}$.

2. If a point is on the perpendicular bisector of a segment, then it is equidistant from the endpoints (Perpendicular Bisector Conjecture).

INVESTIGATION 2

INVESTIGATE

1. A point not on a segment's perpendicular bisector is not equidistant from the segment's endpoints.

2. If a point is equidistant from the endpoints of a segment, then it is on the perpendicular bisector of the segment (Converse of the Perpendicular Bisector Conjecture).

EXPLORE MORE

1. Draw a segment. Construct its midpoint. Select the midpoint and the segment and choose **Construct | Perpendicular Line.**

2. $\overleftrightarrow{AB}$ is the perpendicular bisector of $\overline{CC'}$.

Lesson 3.3 • Medians and Altitudes   DEMO

REQUIRED SKETCH

Triangle Segments Demo.gsp

LESSON GUIDE

This demonstration introduces the terms *median* and *altitude* of a triangle.

INVESTIGATE

1. A median of a triangle is a segment connecting the midpoint of a side to the opposite vertex.

2. $\overline{BE}$ falls outside the triangle if $\angle A$ or $\angle C$ is obtuse.

3. An altitude of a triangle is a perpendicular segment from a vertex to the opposite side or the line containing the opposite side.

4. Every triangle has three altitudes and three medians: one of each from each vertex.

LESSON 3.3 • Constructing Perpendiculars to a Line

EXAMPLE SKETCH

Perpendiculars to a Line.gsp

LESSON GUIDE

Lesson 3.3 in the student book provides a second investigation, in which students discover how to construct perpendiculars using patty paper. That investigation does not conclude in a conjecture, so you could replace Lesson 3.3 in the book with this activity. If you do, assign the book's second investigation as homework.

You could also do most of Lesson 3.3 from the book and do this activity as a demonstration using a single computer and an overhead display device.

Because the investigation is so brief, many students may choose to work on the Explore More problem.

SKETCH

This is a very simple construction.

Step 2: Make sure students construct $\overline{CD}$ to a random point D on $\overleftrightarrow{AB}$, not to point A or point B.

INVESTIGATE

1. CD is greater than the distance from point C to the line.

2. Make sure students have nothing else selected when they drag point D. As CD approaches the distance from point C to the line, $\overline{CD}$ approaches being perpendicular to $\overleftrightarrow{AB}$. This will be confirmed when students construct the perpendicular to $\overleftrightarrow{AB}$ through point C. CD is minimized when point D is at the intersection of $\overleftrightarrow{AB}$ and the perpendicular line.

   The shortest distance from a point to a line is measured along the perpendicular from the point to the line (Shortest Distance Conjecture).

EXPLORE MORE

The circle in this sketch represents the 5-mile radius from the sewage plant. Perhaps surprisingly, the optimal location for the house is on one of the river banks (assuming you don't mind walking to the other river through the sewage zone). This is because the sum of distances to two points is minimal from the segment between those points. And because no segment is perpendicular to two nonparallel lines like the rivers, the sum will be minimized if the home is on a segment perpendicular to one of the rivers but at the other endpoint.

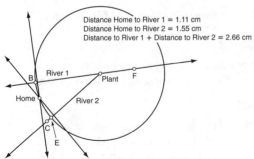

Some students will choose not to construct the perpendicular distances but will construct segments from the home to the intersections of the circle with the river,

arguing that they don't want to fish in a sewage zone any more than they want to live in it.

LESSON 3.4 · Constructing Angle Bisectors

EXAMPLE SKETCH

Angle Bisector.gsp

LESSON GUIDE

In Lesson 3.4 of the student book, the Angle Bisector Conjecture arrives at the end of a construction using patty paper. In a second investigation, students are asked to find a way to construct the angle bisector. If you do this activity in the computer lab, you'll need either to take two days for the lesson or to assign the book investigations as homework. Or you could do this activity as a demonstration on a single computer with an overhead display device.

INVESTIGATE

1. $m\angle BAD = m\angle DAC$

2. If a point is on the bisector of an angle, then it is equidistant from the sides of the angle (Angle Bisector Conjecture).

EXPLORE MORE

1. $\overrightarrow{AC}$ is the bisector of the angle formed by $\overrightarrow{AB}$ and its reflection.

2. In a plane, if a point is equidistant from the sides of an angle, then it is on the angle bisector (Converse of Angle Bisector Conjecture). This is true. To demonstrate, construct an angle and its bisector. Construct a point not on the bisector. Measure the distances from the point to the two sides of the angle. Move the point until those distances are equal. When they are equal, the point will be on the angle bisector. Remind students that they are only representing the case where the point and the angle lie in the same plane. You might ask students to model the converse in space to see why this restriction is necessary for the converse to be true.

3. Answers will vary. One construction is shown on the Explore More page of the example sketch **Angle Bisector.gsp**.

USING YOUR ALGEBRA SKILLS 3 · Slopes of Parallel and Perpendicular Lines

EXAMPLE SKETCH

Parallel Perp Slope.gsp

LESSON GUIDE

This activity covers the information and examples in the student book. Students using this activity will probably write a Perpendicular Slope Conjecture that does not include the term *opposite reciprocal,* as given in the book. They will simply observe that the product of the slopes of perpendicular lines is −1. You may want to spend some time discussing why this conjecture means the same as the one in the book and reviewing the terms *opposite reciprocal* and *negative reciprocal*.

INVESTIGATION 1

SKETCH

Step 1: There are many ways to construct the point of intersection. You can carefully place a point at that spot (drag the lines to make sure the point is anchored correctly), you can click on the spot with the **Arrow** tool, or you can select both lines and choose **Construct | Intersection.**

Step 2: To measure an angle, select three points on the angle, making sure the middle point is the vertex.

INVESTIGATE

1. If two lines have equal slopes, then they are parallel.

INVESTIGATION 2

SKETCH

Step 1: To construct the parallel line, select $\overleftrightarrow{AB}$ and point C and choose **Construct | Parallel Line.**

INVESTIGATE

1. If two lines are parallel, then they have equal slopes.

2. Two lines are parallel if and only if their slopes are equal (Parallel Slope Property).

INVESTIGATION 3

SKETCH

Step 3: To construct a perpendicular to a line and through a point, select the line and the point and choose **Construct | Perpendicular Line.**

INVESTIGATE

1. If two lines are perpendicular, then the product of their slopes is −1.

INVESTIGATION 4

INVESTIGATE

1. If two lines have slopes whose product is −1, then the lines must be perpendicular.

2. Two lines are perpendicular if and only if their slopes have a product of −1 (Perpendicular Slope Property, with different wording).

EXPLORATION · Perspective Drawing

EXAMPLE SKETCH

Perspective.gsp

LESSON GUIDE

The Exploration here skips straight to two-point perspective. Use this activity in place of or as an extension to the Exploration in the student book. Students generally enjoy doing perspective drawing.

SKETCH

Step 1: Hold down the Shift key while constructing the horizon line and front edge, to make it easy to make horizontal and vertical segments.

Step 10: Students can stop here if they're content with bottomless boxes. Students should drag the front edge above the horizon line just to see that the box has no bottom.

INVESTIGATE

Possible answer: As you move the horizon line, you see the box from different heights. When the horizon is above the box, you see the box from above; and when it's below, you see the box from below. If you move one of the vanishing points farther away from the other, you stretch the box; and if you move it closer, the box appears to shrink.

EXPLORE MORE

(Not on student worksheet.) Students can create all kinds of more complicated drawings of houses, office buildings, or whole city blocks using two-point perspective. You can have students try boxes with one-point perspective (viewing a front face instead of a front edge). See the Cabin page in the example sketch **Perspective.gsp.**

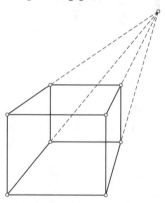

A box with one-point perspective

LESSON 3.7 · Constructing Points of Concurrency

EXAMPLE SKETCH

Concurrency Points.gsp, pages Angle Bisectors, Perpendicular Bisectors, Altitudes, and Explore More.

LESSON GUIDE

This activity replaces the investigations in Lesson 3.7 of the student book. In the book, students investigate all three points of concurrency in Investigation 1; then they return to the incenter and circumcenter in Investigation 2. Here, each of these points has a separate investigation.

The three investigations may be too much to get through in a class period. Consider several options, depending on your students' proficiency with Sketchpad and the length of your class period: (1) Have all students do the angle bisectors investigation and then assign each group one or the other of the remaining two investigations. (2) Divide the three investigations among different groups. (3) Have all students start with the first investigation and go as far as they can. Tell them not to worry if they don't finish.

If you are short on time, or your students don't have much experience using Sketchpad, you might use the Demonstration Point of Concurrency that follows this activity. Whichever option you choose, allow time at the end of the period or in the next class meeting for students to share, and make sure that students have seen demonstrations of every conjecture. In particular, don't skip the Explore More, which relates the circumcenter of a triangle to the circle circumscribed about the triangle, and the incenter to the inscribed circle in the triangle.

Each investigation has a second Sketch section in which students save a tool to make a point of concurrency. Doing these sections is a good way to introduce students to **Custom** tools, but skipping them can save time and the logistics hassle of giving each student a place to store sketches. To use the four tools they construct in Lessons 3.7 and 3.8, students must have access to sketches containing them. Even if you do have students make and save tools, you can avoid trouble by making sure each computer has access to the sketch **Triangle Centers.gsp** in the **Custom Tools** folder on the CD.

INVESTIGATION 1

SKETCH

Step 3: Select the three vertices, with point *B* the second selection.

Step 4: Select the two rays and choose **Construct | Intersection.** Or just click on the intersection with the **Arrow** tool or the **Point** tool. Sketchpad doesn't allow construction of a point at the intersection of three objects, so if students get ahead of the instructions and construct the third angle bisector, the **Arrow** tool or **Point** tool will actually construct the intersection of only two of the lines.

Step 6: Students could choose either the **Arrow** tool or the **Text** tool. The finger of the tool needs to be positioned over the label. When it's correctly positioned, an "A" appears inside the hand.

Step 7: You might have the students name the point *Incenter* for clarity. This label will appear when the **Custom** tool **Incenter** is used.

Step 8: Rather than having students create a new sketch for each investigation, you might have them create a single multi-page sketch. From the File menu, choose

Document Options. Choose Add Page and add three additional blank pages to the sketch. Change the page names to appropriate titles: Angle Bisectors, Perpendicular Bisectors, Altitudes, and Explore More.

INVESTIGATE

1. The third angle bisector passes through the point of intersection of the first two.

2. Three random lines would probably intersect in three different points—not in one point. The three angle bisectors of a triangle are concurrent (Angle Bisector Concurrency Conjecture).

3. The incenter of a triangle is equidistant from the triangle's three sides (Incenter Conjecture).

INVESTIGATION 2

SKETCH

Step 2: It helps if the triangle is acute so that the intersection of the perpendicular bisectors will at least start out inside the triangle.

Step 3: Students can select both segments and choose **Construct | Midpoints** to construct both midpoints simultaneously.

Step 5: Use the method described in Step 4.

Step 6: Select the two lines and choose **Construct | Intersection.** Or just click on the intersection with the **Arrow** tool or the **Point** tool. Sketchpad doesn't allow construction of a point at the intersection of three objects, so if students get ahead of the instructions and construct the third angle bisector, the **Arrow** tool or **Point** tool will actually construct an intersection of only two of the lines.

Step 8: Position the finger of the **Arrow** tool or the **Text** tool directly over the label and double-click. Use *Ci* instead of *C* to differentiate this point from the centroid, which students construct in Lesson 3.8. Or, students can just label the point *Circumcenter.*

INVESTIGATE

1. The three perpendicular bisectors of a triangle are concurrent (Perpendicular Bisector Concurrency Conjecture). For an acute triangle, the point of concurrency falls inside the triangle. For an obtuse triangle, the point of concurrency falls outside the triangle. For a right triangle, the point of concurrency falls at the midpoint of the hypotenuse.

2. The circumcenter of a triangle is equidistant from the triangle's three vertices (Circumcenter Conjecture).

INVESTIGATION 3

SKETCH

Step 2: It helps if the triangle is acute so that the intersection of the altitudes will at least start out inside the triangle.

Step 4: Use the method described in Step 3.

Step 5: Select the two lines and choose **Construct | Intersection.** Or just click on the intersection with the **Arrow** tool or the **Point** tool. Sketchpad doesn't allow construction of a point at the intersection of three objects, so if students get ahead of the instructions and construct the third angle bisector, the **Arrow** tool or **Point** tool will actually construct the intersection of only two of the lines.

Step 7: Position the finger of the **Arrow** tool or the **Text** tool directly over the label and double-click.

INVESTIGATE

1. The three altitudes of a triangle are concurrent (Altitude Concurrency Conjecture). For an acute triangle, the point of concurrency falls inside the triangle. For an obtuse triangle, the point of concurrency falls outside the triangle. For a right triangle, the point of concurrency falls at the vertex of the right angle.

EXPLORE MORE

1. The circumcenter is the center of the circumscribed circle because it is equidistant from the triangle's three vertices.

2. By following these steps, students will draw a circle that is inscribed in the triangle, as long as they don't change the triangle. The incenter is the center of the inscribed circle because it is equidistant from the triangle's three sides. To construct an inscribed circle that will stay inscribed, construct a perpendicular from the incenter to any side of the triangle. Then construct the circle to the intersection of this side and the perpendicular.

LESSONS 3.7 AND 3.8 · Points of Concurrency   DEMO

REQUIRED SKETCH

Triangle Points Demo.gsp

LESSON GUIDE

This demonstration covers the material in Lessons 3.7 and 3.8 of the student book and continues in the demonstration The Euler Segment. There are many questions to answer, but students can go as far as they choose (or as far as you give them time to go).

INVESTIGATE

1. Yes   **2.** 1 : 2   **3.** Yes

4. Inside an acute triangle, outside an obtuse triangle, and at the right angle vertex of a right triangle

5. Yes

6. Possible answer: Any point on an angle bisector is equidistant from the sides of the angle. So the point

at the intersection of the three angle bisectors is equidistant from all three sides of the triangle. Therefore, a circle that has that distance for its radius will be inscribed in the triangle.

7. Yes

8. Inside an acute triangle, outside an obtuse triangle, and at the midpoint of the hypotenuse of a right triangle

9. Possible answer: Any point on the perpendicular bisector of a segment is equidistant from the endpoints of the segment. The circumcenter is on all three of the perpendicular bisectors of the sides of the triangle, so it is equidistant from all three vertices of the triangle. Therefore, a circle centered at the circumcenter that passes through one vertex of the triangle will pass through all three, circumscribing the triangle.

LESSON 3.7 · The Nine-Point Circle   EXT

EXAMPLE SKETCH

Nine Point.gsp

LESSON GUIDE

Students construct the nine-point circle. The directions are involved. You might have students work in pairs, with one student reading the instructions while the other does the construction. They could trade roles after Step 4 or 5.

Alternatively, you might have students use the pre-made example sketch **Nine Point.gsp** to answer the questions. In this case, have them describe the nine points on the circle before they answer the questions.

The example sketch has buttons that perform the constructions needed for Questions 3 and 4.

Step 6: It's easiest to construct the segment, then choose **Construct | Midpoint** while the segment is still selected.

INVESTIGATE

1. Isosceles; the point at which the altitude intersects the base and the midpoint of the base.

2. Equilateral: The foot of each altitude coincides with a midpoint, so only six of the nine points are visible. Right: The feet of two altitudes and the midpoint between the right angle vertex and the orthocenter all coincide at the right angle vertex, so only five of the nine points are visible. Isosceles right: The foot of the third altitude coincides with the midpoint of a side, so only four of the nine points are visible.

3. The inscribed circle is internally tangent to the nine-point circle.

4. The circumscribed circle has radius twice that of the nine-point circle.

LESSON 3.8 · The Centroid

EXAMPLE SKETCH

Concurrency Points.gsp, page Medians

LESSON GUIDE

This activity replaces Lesson 3.8 in the student book. The example sketch is the same as Lesson 3.7. If your students did the activity Constructing Points of Concurrency and saved their work in a multi-page sketch, you might have them add an additional page for this activity.

INVESTIGATION 1

SKETCH

Step 4: Select the two medians and choose **Construct | Intersection.** Or just click on the intersection with the **Arrow** tool or the **Point** tool. Sketchpad doesn't allow construction of a point at the intersection of three objects, so if students get ahead of the instructions and construct the third median, the **Arrow** tool or **Point** tool will actually construct the intersection of only two of the segments.

INVESTIGATE

1. The three medians of a triangle are concurrent (Median Concurrency Conjecture).

INVESTIGATION 2

SKETCH

Step 1: The finger of the **Arrow** tool or the **Text** tool needs to be positioned over the label. When it's correctly positioned, an "A" appears inside the hand. Change the label to *Ce* instead of just *C* to differentiate it from the circumcenter. Or, just label it *Centroid*.

INVESTIGATE

1. The centroid of a triangle divides each median into two parts so that the distance from the centroid to the vertex is twice the distance from the centroid to the midpoint (Centroid Conjecture). Students can confirm this by using the calculator on these distances.

EXPLORATION · The Euler Segment   DEMO

REQUIRED SKETCH

Triangle Points Demo.gsp

LESSON GUIDE

This demonstration builds on the Points of Concurrency demonstration.

INVESTIGATE

1. Incenter

2. Yes; circumcenter and orthocenter

3. Centroid. It divides the segment into two parts whose lengths are in a 2:1 ratio.

4. Isosceles

5. Equilateral

6. No

7. In a right triangle, the orthocenter falls at the right angle vertex and the circumcenter falls at the midpoint of the hypotenuse.

EXPLORATION · The Euler Line

REQUIRED SKETCH

Triangle Centers.gsp

EXAMPLE SKETCH

Euler Line.gsp

LESSON GUIDE

This activity replaces the Exploration in the student book. Students use the four tools they made in Lessons 3.7 and 3.8. If students didn't create all of these tools themselves, they will need access to the sketch **Triangle Centers.gsp** in the **Custom Tools** folder on the CD. Even if students did create and save the tools, it might be easier logistically to make the **Custom Tools** folder accessible to them.

If your students saved their work for the activities Constructing Points of Concurrency and The Centroid in a single multi-page sketch, you might have them add an additional page for this activity.

SKETCH

Step 2: The document(s) that contain the four triangle tools now need to be open. You might want to demonstrate how to find and use one of them.

INVESTIGATE

1. The circumcenter, the centroid, and the orthocenter are the three points of concurrency that always lie on the Euler line (Euler Line Conjecture).

2. All four points are collinear in isosceles triangles.

3. All four points are coincident in equilateral triangles.

4. The orthocenter and the circumcenter are the endpoints of the Euler segment. The centroid lies between them.

5. The centroid divides the Euler segment into two parts so that the smaller part is half as long as the larger part (Euler Segment Conjecture).

REQUIRED SKETCH

Nagel Segment.gsp

EXAMPLE SKETCH

Nagel Point.gsp

LESSON GUIDE

This extension explores another point of concurrency, the Nagel point, and its related segment, the Nagel segment. The construction is fairly time-consuming. You might have students do Steps 2–6, to see how the construction works, and then use the example sketch Nagel Point to answer the questions. Or, students can use the construction in Steps 2–6 to define a **Custom** tool. The required sketch is used for the investigation of the Nagel segment.

INVESTIGATION 1

SKETCH

Step 5: It's important that the circle be constructed through point *I*. Have students drag the triangle to test that the circle is tangent to both the triangle side and the extensions of the other two triangle sides.

Step 6: Here the angle bisectors and perpendicular bisector are hidden to clean up the sketch. You might leave these showing as dashed rays and lines if you want students to see them as reminders for the subsequent constructions. To create a **Custom** tool, select, in order, points *A*, *B*, and *C*, and the orange segment *AI*, the dashed rays, and the circle along with its center and points of tangency. Press the **Custom** tool button and select **Create New Tool.** Give the tool a name, such as *Excircle Segment.*

Step 8: If some points do not have labels showing, you may need to first choose **Show Labels** and then **Hide Labels.** Again, this is done to keep the sketch relatively uncluttered.

INVESTIGATE

1. If you construct a segment from each vertex of a triangle to the point of tangency of the excircle tangent to the opposite side, then the three segments are concurrent.

2. Answers will vary. The Nagel point is never outside or on the triangle because it lies on segments that are always inside the triangle.

INVESTIGATION 2

SKETCH

If your students did the activities Constructing Points of Concurrency and The Centroid, they can use their **Custom** tools to add the incenter, orthocenter, circumcenter, and centroid to the sketch from the previous investigation. Otherwise, use the sketch **Nagel Segment.gsp.**

INVESTIGATE

1. Incenter and centroid

2. The incenter and Nagel point are always the endpoints of the Nagel segment.

3. The centroid divides the Nagel segment into noncongruent segments so that the shorter segment is half the length of the longer segment.

CHAPTER 4

LESSON 4.1 • The Triangle Sum   **DEMO**

REQUIRED SKETCH

Triangle Sum Demo.gsp

LESSON GUIDE

This demonstration is equivalent to the investigation of Lesson 4.1, in which students tear off the angles of a triangle and arrange them along a straight line to make the Triangle Sum Conjecture.

Step 6: You can also drag the vertices of the original triangle *ABC* and observe how the rotated triangles move with it.

INVESTIGATE

1. 180°

2. 180°

3. When a line parallel to a side of the triangle is constructed through the vertex of the opposite angle, it forms two additional angles, each of which is congruent to one of the other two angles in the triangle. (The parallel line forms two pairs of corresponding angles.) Because the three angles form a straight line, the sum of their measures is 180°.

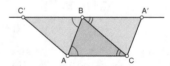

LESSON 4.1 • Triangle Sum Conjecture

EXAMPLE SKETCH

Triangle Sum.gsp

LESSON GUIDE

Use this lesson in place of or as an extension to Lesson 4.1 in the student book. This lesson covers only the first part of the investigation in the book. If you replace Lesson 4.1 with this one, do the rest of the investigation as a follow-along demonstration or assign it as homework.

1. The sum is always 180°.

2. The sum of the measures of the angles in a triangle is 180° (Triangle Sum Conjecture).

EXPLORE MORE

1. **a.** They are congruent to the three angles of the triangle.

   b. Possible answer: $\overleftrightarrow{ED} \parallel \overline{AB}$, so $\angle ACD \cong \angle BAC$ and $\angle BCE \cong \angle ABC$ by AIA. Therefore, $m\angle ACD + m\angle BCA + m\angle BCE = 180°$ $= m\angle CAB + m\angle BCA + m\angle ABC$.

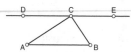

2. **a.** A third congruent triangle will fill the space between the two triangles.

   b. They are the three angles of the triangle, and they form a straight line.

   c. By demonstrating that the three angles of the triangle form a straight line and therefore sum to 180°

3. Answers will vary. This previews Lesson 5.1, Polygon Sum Conjecture.

4. One possible approach is to rotate one side about an endpoint successively by each angle of the given triangle. If the angles of rotation are all marked in a consistent order, the image of the segment will end up along a line with the original segment.

LESSON 4.2 · Properties of Isosceles Triangles

EXAMPLE SKETCH

Isosceles Triangle.gsp

LESSON GUIDE

Use this activity in place of or as an extension to Lesson 4.2 in the student book.

INVESTIGATION 1

SKETCH

You may want to have students make an isosceles triangle **Custom** tool.

INVESTIGATE

1. Two of the sides are radii of the same circle.

2. The measures of the two angles are always equal.

3. If a triangle is isosceles, then its base angles are congruent (Isosceles Triangle Conjecture).

INVESTIGATION 2

INVESTIGATE

1. The triangle appears isosceles.

2. $BD = AD$

3. If a triangle has two congruent angles, then it is an isosceles triangle (Converse of the Isosceles Triangle Conjecture).

EXPLORE MORE

An equilateral triangle is equiangular, and, conversely, an equiangular triangle is equilateral (Equilateral/ Equiangular Triangle Conjecture). This conjecture is presented formally and proven in Lesson 4.8.

LESSON 4.3 · Triangle Inequalities

EXAMPLE SKETCH

Triangle Inequalities.gsp

LESSON GUIDE

Use this lesson in place of or as an extension to Lesson 4.3 in the student book. Students will need to know the terms *remote interior angles*, *adjacent interior angles*, and *exterior angles* to do Investigation 3. See page 217 of the student book.

INVESTIGATION 1

INVESTIGATE

1. The three segments no longer form a triangle.

2. No; if the sum of two sides is shorter than the third side, it is impossible for the two ends to connect.

3. The sum of the lengths of any two sides of a triangle is greater than the length of the third side (Triangle Inequality Conjecture).

INVESTIGATION 2

INVESTIGATE

1.

Longest side	Largest angle
$\overline{AB}$	$\angle C$
$\overline{AC}$	$\angle B$
$\overline{BC}$	$\angle A$

Shortest side	Smallest angle
$\overline{AB}$	$\angle C$
$\overline{AC}$	$\angle B$
$\overline{BC}$	$\angle A$

2. In a triangle, the longest side is opposite the angle with greatest measure and the shortest side is opposite the angle with least measure (Side-Angle Inequality Conjecture).

INVESTIGATION 3

INVESTIGATE

1. The measure of an exterior angle of a triangle is equal to the sum of the measures of the remote interior angles (Triangle Exterior Angle Conjecture).

EXPLORE MORE

1. The sum of the lengths of any three segments must be greater than the length of the fourth segment.

2. Answers will vary.

3. Translating the interior along a vector from A to B, then rotating it through 180° about the midpoint of $\overline{BC}$ will fill in the exterior angle with the adjacent interior angles of the triangle.

LESSON 4.4 · Are There Congruence Shortcuts?

REQUIRED SKETCH

Congruence Shortcuts.gsp, pages SSS, SAS, and SSA.

LESSON GUIDE

Use this lesson in place of or as an extension to Lesson 4.4 in the student book. The SSA example is done as an investigation here. Students use prepared sketches for these investigations.

INVESTIGATION 1

SKETCH

Step 1: Some students may make the triangle on the right into a reflection of the triangle on the left. To confirm that the two triangles are congruent, they can either print the triangles or use Sketchpad to measure the three angles.

INVESTIGATE

1. No. (They may appear to have different shapes if they are reflections of each other.)

2. Yes

3. If the three sides of one triangle are congruent to the three sides of another triangle, then the triangles are congruent (SSS Congruence Conjecture).

INVESTIGATION 2

INVESTIGATE

1. No. (They may appear to have different shapes if they are reflections of each other.)

2. Yes

3. If two sides and the angle between them in one triangle are congruent to two sides and the angle between them in another triangle, then the triangles are congruent (SAS Congruence Conjecture).

INVESTIGATION 3

INVESTIGATE

1. Yes   2. No

3. It is possible that two sides and the angle not between them in one triangle are congruent to the corresponding two sides and angle in another triangle without the two triangles being congruent.

LESSON 4.5 · Are There Other Congruence Shortcuts?

REQUIRED SKETCHES

Congruence Shortcuts.gsp, pages ASA and AAA

LESSON GUIDE

Use this lesson in place of, or as an extension to, Lesson 4.5 in the student book. The AAA example is done as an investigation here. There is no investigation for SAA. You might ask students to do a Sketchpad construction or remind them of the Third Angle Conjecture. Students use prepared sketches for these investigations.

INVESTIGATION 1

SKETCH

Step 3: Some students may make the triangle on the right into a reflection of the triangle on the left. To confirm that the two triangles are congruent, they can either print the triangles or use Sketchpad to measure the three sides.

INVESTIGATE

1. No. (They may appear to have different shapes if they are reflections of each other.)

2. Yes

3. If two angles and the side between them in one triangle are congruent to two angles and the side between them in another triangle, then the triangles are congruent (ASA Congruence Conjecture).

INVESTIGATION 2

INVESTIGATE

1. Yes

2. No

3. The three angles of one triangle may be congruent to the three angles of another triangle without the two triangles being congruent.

LESSON 4.8 · Special Triangle Conjectures

EXAMPLE SKETCH

Special Triangle Conjectures.gsp

LESSON GUIDE

Use this activity as an extension to Lesson 4.8 in the student book, but not in place of it. This activity covers the Vertex Angle Bisector Conjecture, but not the Equilateral/Equiangular Triangle Conjecture or any proofs.

INVESTIGATE

1. $\overline{AD}$ is the altitude of the vertex angle.

2. D is the midpoint of $\overline{CB}$.

3. $\overline{AD}$ is the median of the vertex angle.

4. In an isosceles triangle, the bisector of the vertex angle is also the altitude and the median to the base (Vertex Angle Bisector Conjecture).

EXPLORE MORE

1. The converse is true: If the bisector of the vertex angle is also the altitude and the median to the base, then the triangle is an isosceles triangle.

2. An isosceles triangle is equilateral if the angle bisector, median, and altitude of a nonvertex angle are concurrent.

CHAPTER 5

LESSON 5.1 · Polygon Sum Conjecture

EXAMPLE SKETCH

Polygon Sum.gsp

LESSON GUIDE

You can use this activity to replace Lesson 5.1 in the student book. Explore More Questions 1 and 2 cover the same topics as Take Another Look activity 1 at the end of Chapter 5 in the book.

INVESTIGATE

1. The sum stays constant at 360° for convex quadrilaterals. For concave quadrilaterals, the angle sum appears to be less than 360° because Sketchpad does not measure angles greater than 180°. (Adventurous students may even discover *crossed polygons,* or *star polygons,* which have sides that cross. Their angle sums also follow different rules, which students can investigate in the Exploration Star Polygons on pages 266–267 of their book.)

The sum of the measures of the four angles of every quadrilateral is 360° (Quadrilateral Sum Conjecture).

2. Answers may vary. You might want to organize the polygon selection to make sure that different groups investigate different polygons.

3. **and 4.** *n* and the polygon name should correspond. Students could choose a polygon (such as a 13-gon) that does not have a common name. Encourage them to give it their own name.

5. Answers will vary. Give students time to figure out their predictions. There are several valid ways to reason through this problem.

6. Answers will vary. Students may or may not find that their predictions matched their discoveries. For now, they do not need to worry about concave polygons.

7. The sum of the measures of the *n* angles of an *n*-gon is 180° (n − 2) (Polygon Sum Conjecture). It might be useful to have groups record their results on the board so that students can observe the different results from around the class. If students need help, elicit the idea that the sums go up by 180° for every new side. And you can't make a polygon with only one side or only two sides, so you don't get the first 180° until you have three sides. For this reason, you have to subtract 2 from *n* before you multiply it by 180°.

EXPLORE MORE

1. Possible explanation: Each side of the polygon, other than the two adjacent to the common vertex, is opposite that vertex in one of the triangles. So, there are *n* − 2 triangles. Each triangle has an angle sum of 180°, and their angles together make up the angles of the polygon. So, the total angle sum of the polygon is (n − 2)180°.

2. If you consider the caved-in angles as having measures greater than 180°, the Polygon Sum Conjecture holds. You can still divide a concave polygon into *n* − 2 triangles by drawing diagonals. To test the Polygon Sum Conjecture with Sketchpad, students could calculate (360° − the angle measure) for any caved-in angles and use this calculation when they sum all the angle measures.

3. The sum of the angle measures in an octagon is (8 − 2)180° = 1080°. Because all angles of a regular octagon are congruent, each angle must be one-eighth of this total, or 135°. If you rotate a segment and one endpoint about its other endpoint by an angle of 135° and continue this process six more times, you get a regular octagon.

LESSON 5.2 · Exterior Angles   DEMO

REQUIRED SKETCH

Exterior Angles Demo.gsp

LESSON GUIDE

This is a convincing demonstration of why the sum of the measures of one set of exterior angles in any polygon is 360°. The issue of exterior angles in nonconvex polygons can get complicated, so consider offering extra credit for thoughtful responses to Question 3.

INVESTIGATE

1. 360°

2. Yes. It doesn't matter how many sides the polygon has or what shape it is. When it is shrunk to a single point, one set of exterior angles surrounds that point. Thus, the sum of the angle measures is the same as one complete revolution around a point, or 360°.

3. Possible answer: In a nonconvex polygon, one or more interior angles have measure greater than 180°. At each such angle, the "exterior" angle falls inside the triangle. To form a linear pair with the angle whose measure is greater than 180°, the exterior angle has to be subtracted from it. Because its orientation is different from the other exterior angles, it can be considered to have a negative measure, in which case the sum of the exterior angle measures is still 360°.

LESSON 5.2 · Exterior Angles of a Polygon

EXAMPLE SKETCH

Polygon Exterior Angles.gsp

LESSON GUIDE

You can use this activity to replace Lesson 5.2 in the student book. Explore More 1 extends the meaning of the Equiangular Polygon Conjecture by having students construct regular polygons.

INVESTIGATION 1

SKETCH

Step 3: Make sure that students measure exterior angles, not interior angles, and that they measure them all.

INVESTIGATE

1. In any polygon, the sum of the exterior angles is 360°. In order for the Polygon Sum Conjecture to hold for concave polygons, you need to define the exterior angle at a point of concavity to be negative. You can have Sketchpad do this by choosing **Edit | Preferences** and changing the **Angle Units** to be directed degrees. However, with preferences set this way, you need to be more careful about the order in which you select points to measure angles. This further exploration could make a good extension to the demo.

2. The sum of the measures of one set of exterior angles is 360° (Exterior Angle Sum Conjecture).

INVESTIGATION 2

SKETCH

Step 3: Make sure students rotate the endpoints of the segment as well as the segment itself.

Step 4: One possibility is to continue rotating successive segments about successive centers until you arrive back at the starting segment. Students might also use reflections and translations, depending on the symmetry of their particular polygon.

INVESTIGATE

1. Possible answers: hexagon: 120°; heptagon: $128\frac{4}{7}° \approx 128.57°$; octagon: 135°. Students' methods for finding these measures will vary (see the answer to Question 2).

2. Give students time to think about this challenge. The measure of each angle of a regular n-gon can be found by using either of the following formulas: $\frac{(n-2)180°}{n}$ or $180° - \frac{360°}{n}$ (Equiangular Polygon Conjecture). The first formula is the sum of the interior angles divided by the number of angles. The second formula comes from the fact that the interior angle is supplementary to an exterior angle.

3. Probably, though not necessarily

4. One example is a nonsquare rectangle because it has four equal right angles, but sides of different lengths. Any polygon with more than three sides can be equiangular without being equilateral. You can visualize this as taking a regular polygon and stretching it along one or more sets of parallel sides, but leaving the angles unchanged.

EXPLORE MORE

1. This corresponds to the software construction on page 263 of the student book. Encourage all students to try this. It's easy to do, and it's a dazzling demonstration that the sum of these angles is 360°. As you dilate the figure toward any point, the polygon will shrink toward that point, leaving you with only the angles going all the way around a common vertex. You'll want to discuss the fact that when you dilate a polygon, the measures of the angles remain constant. You can measure the exterior angles before you dilate, and students will see that the angle measures don't change.

2. The simplest such example is a rectangle, though you might challenge students to construct a polygon with more sides. There are many ways to construct a rectangle. Here is one interesting way that can be generalized for constructing any equiangular polygon by changing the angle of rotation: Start with a line, and mark one of the control points on the line as a center of rotation. Rotate the line 90°, then construct an independent point on the new line. Mark this new independent point as a center of rotation and rotate the new line 90°. Continue this process until the newest line intersects the original line.

LESSON 5.3 · Kite and Trapezoid Properties

REQUIRED SKETCH

Quad Family.gsp

EXAMPLE SKETCH

Kite and Trapezoid.gsp

LESSON GUIDE

This activity replaces Lesson 5.3 and follows the same steps as the student text. Explore More 4 is the same as Take Another Look activity 7 at the end of the chapter.

You might want to point out to students at the end of these investigations that kite properties hold for rhombuses, and isosceles trapezoid properties hold for rectangles as well.

INVESTIGATION 1

SKETCH

Step 1: If your students need an extra challenge, have them construct their own kite instead of finding it in the prepared sketch. See Explore More 1.

Step 3: To construct the point of intersection, click on that spot with either the **Arrow** tool or the **Point** tool. Also, you can select both segments and choose **Intersection** from the Construct menu.

INVESTIGATE

1. The nonvertex angles of a kite are congruent (Kite Angles Conjecture).

2. The diagonals of a kite are perpendicular (Kite Diagonals Conjecture).

3. The diagonal connecting the vertex angles of a kite is the perpendicular bisector of the other diagonal (Kite Diagonal Bisector Conjecture). Encourage students to measure the four distances from the intersection point of the diagonals to the vertices for confirmation.

4. The vertex angles of a kite are bisected by a diagonal (Kite Angle Bisector Conjecture). Encourage students to measure the smaller angles formed by the diagonals to confirm this.

INVESTIGATION 2

SKETCH

Step 1: If your students need an extra challenge, have them construct their own trapezoid instead of finding it in the prepared sketch. See Explore More 2.

Step 3: If your students need an extra challenge, have them construct their own isosceles trapezoid instead of finding it in the prepared sketch. See Explore More 3.

INVESTIGATE

1. The consecutive angles between the bases of a trapezoid are supplementary (Trapezoid Consecutive Angles Conjecture).

2. The base angles of an isosceles trapezoid are congruent (Isosceles Trapezoid Conjecture).

3. The diagonals of an isosceles trapezoid are congruent (Isosceles Trapezoid Diagonals Conjecture).

EXPLORE MORE

Note on Explore More 1–3: It might be both fun and useful to have students save these polygons as **Custom** tools. To do this, select the polygon, press and hold the **Custom** tool button, and choose **Create New Tool** from the menu. Give the tool an appropriate name. The tool is saved with the sketch. It will be available whenever this sketch is open.

1. A simple way to construct a kite is to reflect an acute triangle across its longest side. Notice that both this construction and the construction in the prepared sketch result in kites that can be manipulated into rhombuses or darts (concave kites), in which case, they no longer satisfy the student book definition of a kite.

2. To construct a trapezoid, create a line parallel to a segment and connect the line to the segment with two more segments. Then hide the line and replace it with a segment. Both this construction and the construction in the prepared sketch result in trapezoids that can be manipulated into parallelograms, in which case, they no longer satisfy the student book definition of a trapezoid.

3. Perhaps the simplest way to construct an isosceles trapezoid is to use reflections. Construct a segment and a mirror line either not intersecting the segment or through any point except the endpoints. Reflect the segment and endpoints across the mirror line and finish the isosceles trapezoid by connecting the appropriate vertices. Both this construction and the construction in the prepared sketch result in isosceles trapezoids that can be manipulated into rectangles, in which case, they no longer satisfy the student book definition of a trapezoid.

4. If you extend the diagonals of the darts so that they always intersect, then all the kite conjectures still hold.

LESSON 5.4 · Properties of Midsegments

REQUIRED SKETCH

Quad Family.gsp

EXAMPLE SKETCH

Midsegment Properties.gsp

LESSON GUIDE

This activity replaces Lesson 5.4 in the student book.

INVESTIGATION 1

INVESTIGATE

1. The three midsegments of a triangle divide it into four congruent triangles (Three Midsegments Conjecture). Encourage students to measure angles and sides to verify that the triangles are congruent. This might be a good time to review the triangle congruency shortcuts: Have students figure out a minimal group of sides and angles that would be sufficient to conclude that all four triangles are congruent. For example, they could measure two pairs of corresponding sides and the included angle on each triangle and use the SAS Congruence Conjecture.

2. Possible answers: The length of the midsegment must be half that of the third side; the two segments are parallel. Give students a chance to notice any of the properties before measuring.

3. A midsegment of a triangle is parallel to the third side and half the length of the third side (Triangle Midsegment Conjecture).

INVESTIGATION 2

SKETCH

Step 1: If your students need an extra challenge, have them construct their own trapezoid instead of finding it in the prepared sketch. To construct a trapezoid, create a line parallel to a segment and connect the line to the segment with two more segments. Then hide the line and replace it with a segment. Both this construction and the construction in the prepared sketch result in trapezoids that can be manipulated into parallelograms, in which case, they no longer satisfy the student book definition of a trapezoid.

Step 2: Select the pair of nonparallel sides and choose **Midpoints** from the Construct menu. Then connect these two midpoints.

INVESTIGATE

1. The midsegment of a trapezoid is parallel to the bases.

2. The midsegment of a trapezoid is equal in length to the average of the lengths of the bases. Encourage students to calculate the average of the lengths of the bases using the calculator.

3. The midsegment of a trapezoid is parallel to the bases and equal in length to the average of the two base lengths (Trapezoid Midsegment Conjecture).

LESSON 5.5 • Properties of Parallelograms

EXAMPLE SKETCH

Parallelogram Properties.gsp

LESSON GUIDE

This activity replaces Lesson 5.5 in the student book.

SKETCH

Step 5: To construct a point of intersection, click at that spot with either the **Arrow** tool or the **Point** tool. Also, you can select both lines and choose **Intersection** from the Construct menu.

INVESTIGATE

1. The opposite angles of a parallelogram are congruent (Parallelogram Opposite Angles Conjecture).

2. The consecutive angles of a parallelogram are supplementary (Parallelogram Consecutive Angles Conjecture).

3. The opposite sides of a parallelogram are congruent (Parallelogram Opposite Sides Conjecture).

4. The diagonals of a parallelogram bisect each other (Parallelogram Diagonals Conjecture).

EXPLORE MORE

Here is one construction method that relies on the Parallelogram Diagonals Conjecture: Draw a segment and find its midpoint. (This will be the first diagonal.) Draw another segment with the midpoint as one of its endpoints. Mark the midpoint as a center and rotate this second segment by 180°. Now you have the second diagonal. Connect the endpoints of the diagonals to create the parallelogram.

A different construction method uses the point similarity of the parallelogram: Construct a triangle and the midpoint of one side. Mark the midpoint as a center of rotation, and rotate the other two sides (and their intersection) about that center by 180°. Hide the third side and its midpoint.

It might be both fun and useful to have students save the parallelogram as a **Custom** tool. To do this, select the parallelogram and choose **Create New Tool** from the Custom Tools menu. Give the tool an appropriate name. The tool is saved with the sketch. The tool will be available whenever this sketch is open.

USING YOUR ALGEBRA SKILLS 5 • Equations of Lines   DEMO

REQUIRED SKETCH

Slope Intercept Demo.gsp

LESSON GUIDE

This demonstration covers some of the material of the Using Your Algebra Skills, but here students don't get practice writing equations of lines given point coordinates. They do discover where the slope and the *y*-intercept appear in the slope-intercept form of the equation of a line. They also discover the equation form for horizontal and vertical lines.

INVESTIGATE

1. *Translate*   **2.** *y-intercept*

3. The constant term   **4.** *Rotate*

5. *slope*   **6.** The coefficient of *x*

7. $y = mx + b$ **8.** Zero

9. $y = 0x + b$, or $y = b$ **10.** $x = 0$

11. Undefined

12. *y*-intercept; a vertical line doesn't intersect the *y*-axis (unless they coincide).

13. $x = c$

14. For any point on a vertical line, the *x*-coordinate is a constant, regardless of the *y*-coordinate.

USING YOUR ALGEBRA SKILLS 5 · Writing Linear Equations

EXAMPLE SKETCH

Equation of a Line.gsp

LESSON GUIDE

This activity covers the same material as the information in the student text.

INVESTIGATE

1. and 2. Give students time to play with this. The line and function plot will coincide.

3. In slope-intercept form, *m* is the slope, and *b* is the *y*-intercept. In intercept form, *b* is the slope and *a* is the *y*-intercept.

EXPLORE MORE

The distance between lines is the length of a segment perpendicular to them, not necessarily vertical. So a pair of parallel lines will be 2 units apart only when the lines are horizontal, with slope 0. As you increase the slope of the lines, the distance between them decreases, and when the lines are vertical, they coincide because the distance between them has diminished to zero.

Here is one possible sequence of steps for constructing a set of parallel lines with *y*-intercepts 2 units apart: Draw a line and construct the point where it intersects the *y*-axis. Translate this point up 2 units by choosing **Transform | Translate.** Then construct a line parallel to the first line through this image point. *Note:* The units used in the translation must match the units of the grid. This will be true as long as the grid retains its original

scale. The only way to scale the grid is to drag the point (1, 0). To avoid scaling the grid accidentally, you can always hide this point.

LESSON 5.6 · Properties of Special Parallelograms

REQUIRED SKETCH

Quad Family.gsp

EXAMPLE SKETCH

Special Parallelograms.gsp

LESSON GUIDE

This activity replaces Lesson 5.6 in the student book. The only part of the lesson not covered here is Investigation 1, in which students learn a specific method of constructing a rhombus. You can replace this investigation with Explore More 1, except that here students must find their own method to construct a rhombus.

INVESTIGATION 1

SKETCH

Step 1: If your students need an extra challenge, have them construct their own rhombus instead of finding it in the prepared sketch. See Explore More 1.

Step 3: To construct a point of intersection, click at that spot with the **Arrow** tool or the **Point** tool. Also, you can select both lines and choose **Intersection** from the Construct menu.

INVESTIGATE

1. The diagonals of a rhombus are perpendicular bisectors of each other (Rhombus Diagonals Conjecture). Encourage students to measure an angle formed by the diagonals to verify that it measures 90°. Also encourage them to measure the four distances from the intersection point of the diagonals to the vertices. To measure distances between a pair of points, select both points and choose **Distance** from the Measure menu.

2. The diagonals of a rhombus bisect the angles of the rhombus (Rhombus Angles Conjecture). Encourage students to measure the smaller angles formed at each vertex to verify that each pair has equal measure.

INVESTIGATION 2

SKETCH

Step 1: If your students need an extra challenge, have them construct their own rectangle instead of finding it in the prepared sketch. See Explore More 2.

Step 3: If your students need an extra challenge, have them construct their own square instead of finding it in the prepared sketch. See Explore More 3.

1. The angles of a rectangle are congruent and measure 90°.

2. The diagonals of a rectangle are congruent and bisect each other (Rectangle Diagonals Conjecture). Encourage students to measure both diagonals.

3. Every conjecture that holds for a rectangle or a rhombus also holds for a square because every square is a rhombus and a rectangle.

4. a. A square is an equiangular rhombus (or a rectangular rhombus).

   b. A square is an equilateral rectangle.

5. The diagonals of a square are congruent and perpendicular, and they bisect each other (Square Diagonals Conjecture).

EXPLORE MORE

Note on Explore More 1–3: It might be both fun and useful to have students save these polygons as **Custom** tools. To do this, select the polygon and choose **Create New Tool** from the Custom Tools menu. Give the tool an appropriate name. The tool is saved with the sketch. The tool will be available whenever the sketch is open.

1. Possible method: Construct a circle *AB*, then construct a radius from *A* to *B* as well as another radius $\overline{AC}$. Now construct circles *CA* and *BA* and find their point of intersection. Finish your rhombus by constructing the remaining sides. Another method, which uses reflective symmetry, is like that of the kite in Explore More 1 of Lesson 5.3, except that it begins with an isosceles triangle. (The congruent sides of the triangle can themselves be obtained using a reflection.)

2. Possible method: Construct a segment. Select the segment and both endpoints and choose **Perpendicular Line** from the Construct menu. Construct a free point on one of the lines. Select this new point and the original segment and choose **Parallel Line** from the Construct menu. Construct the last remaining vertex of the rectangle, hide all the lines, and replace them with segments. Another method, which uses point symmetry, is like that of the parallelogram in Explore More of Lesson 5.5, except that you begin with a right triangle.

3. Here is a possible method that makes use of the properties of both a rectangle and a rhombus: Construct a segment and its midpoint. Mark the midpoint as a center. Select the segment and its endpoints and rotate the segment by 90°. You have just created the diagonals of a square. Connect the endpoints to create the square. Another method, which uses symmetry, follows the method of either

the rhombus or the rectangle, but begins with an isosceles right triangle and either reflecting or rotating.

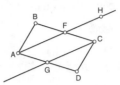

4. If students have a parallelogram tool, they can save time by using it here.

   a. The angle bisectors of opposite angles of a parallelogram are parallel. Possible explanation: Because opposite angles of a parallelogram are congruent, $m\angle BAD = m\angle DCB$. Therefore, the two angle bisectors create four smaller congruent angles. One pair of these is $\angle FAD$ and $\angle FCG$. Opposite sides of a parallelogram are parallel, so $m\angle FAD = m\angle HFC$ because these are corresponding angles. Therefore, $m\angle FCG = m\angle HFC$. And because these are opposite interior angles of the two angle bisectors with $\overline{BC}$ as the transversal, the angle bisectors are parallel.

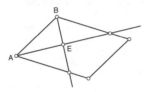

   b. Angle bisectors of adjacent angles of a parallelogram are perpendicular. Possible explanation: Adjacent angles in a parallelogram are supplementary, and the angle bisectors split these adjacent angles in half. So, $\angle ABE$ and $\angle EAB$ are complementary. The remaining angle in $\triangle AEB$ must measure 90° because the first 90° has already been used up by the complementary angles. Therefore, the angle bisectors are perpendicular.

LESSON 5.7 • Variations on the Crane   EXT

contributed by Etsuo Hayashi

EXAMPLE SKETCH

Crane.gsp

LESSON GUIDE

Many students have folded origami cranes. In this extension students fold a traditional crane, then use The Geometer's Sketchpad to explore what other shapes can be used to make a crane.

ADDITIONAL MATERIALS

plain paper, patty paper, origami paper, or gift wrap

INVESTIGATION

Step 1: You might have students use plain paper or patty paper to make their square cranes, then use origami paper or gift wrap to make their quadrilateral cranes.

Step 3: It is $\frac{1}{4}$ the size of the original square.

Step 5: Rhombus; the diagonals are perpendicular bisectors of each other.

INVESTIGATE

1. Four lines of symmetry: $\overline{AC}$, $\overline{GJ}$, $\overline{BD}$, and $\overline{FH}$.

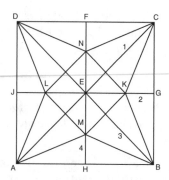

2. The actual crane has one line of symmetry, running from front to back; this is diagonal $\overline{AC}$ in Question 1.

3. Answers will vary. In a nonsquare pattern, points D, E, and B do not have to be collinear, but $\overline{DE}$ must be the bisector of $\angle ADC$, and $\overline{BE}$ the bisector of $\angle ABC$. Also, $\overline{AL}$ must be the bisector of $\angle JAE$, and so on. Students may think H has to be the midpoint of $\overline{AB}$, but actually points E and M determine $\overline{EH}$; points E, H, and F do not have to be collinear.

Step 15: It will always be symmetric about diagonal $\overline{AC}$.

Step 16: These are $\overline{DE}$ and $\overline{BE}$ in the drawing for Question 1.

Step 19: These are $\overline{EH}$, $\overline{EG}$, $\overline{EF}$, and $\overline{EJ}$ in the drawing for Question 1.

INVESTIGATE

4. Differences will vary.

5. Square, rhombus, kite, dart (concave kite), or isosceles triangle.

CHAPTER 6

LESSON 6.1 · Tangents to Circles   DEMO

REQUIRED SKETCH

Tangents to Circles Demo.gsp

LESSON GUIDE

This demonstration reveals the Tangent Conjecture and the Tangent Segments Conjecture by starting with secant rays. It can be used to replace or provide a second approach to the material in Lesson 6.1. The converse of

the Tangent Conjecture is also covered here, in more depth than it is covered in the student book. Therefore, at least the second half of this demonstration is highly recommended.

INVESTIGATION 1

SKETCH

Step 2: As the ray through point B becomes tangent to the circle, the two radii to the intersection points should become one segment. Similarly for point C.

INVESTIGATE

1. When both rays are tangent, $BD = CD$. This is true for any starting point for D. Tangent segments to a circle from a point outside the circle are congruent (Tangent Segments Conjecture).

2. They are perpendicular, no matter where D is. A tangent to a circle is perpendicular to the radius drawn to the point of tangency (Tangent Conjecture).

3. If you construct a line that is perpendicular to a radius and goes through the point where the radius touches the circle, then that line will be tangent to the circle (converse of the Tangent Conjecture). You can check this by constructing a perpendicular to a radius and seeing if that perpendicular line intersects the circle more than once.

INVESTIGATION 2

INVESTIGATE

4. Once; no

5. The answer to question 4 suggests that the converse of the Tangent Conjecture is true.

6. Given a circle, construct any radius. Then construct perpendicular to the radius through the radial endpoint.

LESSON 6.1 · Tangent Properties

EXAMPLE SKETCH

Tangents.gsp

LESSON GUIDE

This activity replaces Lesson 6.1 in the student book, but students should look in the book for the poem that opens the lesson.

INVESTIGATION 1

SKETCH

Step 3: Make sure students measure the correct angle. They need to measure the angle whose vertex is the radius endpoint.

INVESTIGATE

1. Depending on the precision with which students are displaying angle measurements, the measure of

$\angle CBA$ should be very close to 90°. A tangent to a circle is perpendicular to the radius drawn to the point of tangency (Tangent Conjecture).

INVESTIGATION 2

The steps presented here actually use the *converse* of the Tangent Conjecture, which is covered in slightly more depth in the preceding demonstration. You might want to take an extra moment to discuss the converse as a class.

SKETCH

Step 4: Use the method described in Step 2.

Step 5: Students may need to do some dragging to bring this intersection onto their screens.

INVESTIGATE

1. Tangent segments to a circle from a point outside the circle are congruent (Tangent Segments Conjecture).

LESSON 6.2 • Chord Properties

EXAMPLE SKETCH

Chords.gsp

LESSON GUIDE

This activity replaces Lesson 6.2 in the student book. It omits Investigation 1, in which students define *central angle* and *inscribed angle,* so you might want to go over those terms before beginning this activity.

INVESTIGATION 1

SKETCH

Step 5: Students can look at the prompter in the bottom left corner of the sketch to confirm that they're releasing the mouse button at an intersection.

Step 6: Be sure students don't hide the wrong circle. The circle to be hidden is shown dashed in the figure.

INVESTIGATE

1. If two chords in a circle are congruent, then they determine two central angles that are congruent (Chord Central Angles Conjecture).

2. If two chords in a circle are congruent, then their intercepted arcs are congruent (Chord Arcs Conjecture). *Note:* This conjecture follows directly from the Chord Central Angles Conjecture.

INVESTIGATION 2

INVESTIGATE

1. The perpendicular intersects the chord at the chord's midpoint. The perpendicular from the center of a circle to a chord is the perpendicular bisector of the chord (Perpendicular to a Chord Conjecture).

2. Two congruent chords in a circle are equally distant from the center of the circle (Chord Distance to Center Conjecture).

INVESTIGATION 3

INVESTIGATE

1. The perpendicular bisector of a chord passes through the center of the circle (Perpendicular Bisector of a Chord Conjecture).

2. Construct two chords and their perpendicular bisectors. The circle's center is the point where these perpendicular bisectors intersect.

EXPLORE MORE

1. Because all radii of a circle are congruent, two congruent chords define two congruent triangles by SSS. Thus, the central angles they define are congruent by CPCTC.

2. A longer chord in a circle is closer to the center of the circle. The longest possible chords in a circle are diameters.

3. If two congruent segments are chords of noncongruent circles, the chord in the larger circle will define a smaller central angle. You can return to this question after students have studied trigonometry and show that the measurement of a central angle equals $2 \tan^{-1} \frac{l}{2r}$, where l is the length of the chord and r is the radius of the circle. As r increases, the value of this expression decreases.

Lesson 6.2 • Intersecting Tangents Conjecture   DEMO

REQUIRED SKETCH

Intersecting Tangents Demo.gsp.

LESSON GUIDE

Use this demonstration to replace or supplement the Mini-Investigation in Exercise 23 of Lesson 6.2.

INVESTIGATE

1. The Tangent Conjecture implies that $\overrightarrow{PA} \perp \overline{QA}$ and $\overrightarrow{PB} \perp \overline{QB}$.

2. $m\angle APB = 20°$ when $m\angle AQB = 160°$.

3. $m\angle APB = 70°$ when $m\widehat{AB} = 110°$.

4. The measure of the angle formed by two intersecting tangents to a circle is 180° minus the measure of the intercepted arc. (In other words, the angle formed by two intersecting tangents and the angle formed by the corresponding radii are supplementary.)

5. By the Quadrilateral Sum Conjecture, $m\angle P + m\angle 2 + m\angle 3 + m\angle 4 = 360°$. Because $\angle 3$ and $\angle 4$ are both right angles, $m\angle P + m\angle 3 = 180°$. By the

definition of arc measure, $m\angle 3 = m\overarc{AB}$, so $m\angle P + m\overarc{AB} = 180°$.

LESSON 6.3 • Arcs and Angles

EXAMPLE SKETCH

Arcs and Angles.gsp

LESSON GUIDE

This activity replaces Lesson 6.3 in the student book. The first three investigations in the lesson are combined in this activity. Here, the inscribed angle is defined by its relationship to the intercepted arc, rather than to the central angle, as in the book.

INVESTIGATION 1

SKETCH

Step 5: Selection order is important here. Sketchpad constructs arcs defined by two points in counter-clockwise order around the circle. Arcs so defined are not necessarily minor arcs!

Step 6: You can tell whether a click selects the arc or the circle by where the selection indicators appear. If clicking selects the circle, just click again to select the arc that overlaps the circle.

INVESTIGATE

1. The measure of an inscribed angle in a circle is half the measure of the arc it intercepts (Inscribed Angle Conjecture).

2. The computer isn't broken. Dragging point C doesn't change the arc; thus, it doesn't change the measurement of the inscribed angle that intercepts it. Students often don't think of a single dynamic angle as representing many angles. Instead, they think of it as a single angle that moves. So, they may need to construct a second angle to be convinced of this conjecture: Inscribed angles that intercept the same arc are congruent (Inscribed Angles Intercepting Arcs Conjecture).

3. $m\angle DCB$ should be close to 90°. Angles inscribed in a semicircle are right angles (Angles Inscribed in a Semicircle Conjecture).

INVESTIGATION 2

SKETCH

Step 3: Students should double-check that they've measured the four different angles in the quadrilateral. No two of the four angle measurements should have the same middle letter. If they do, students are apt to jump to an incorrect conclusion that pairs of angles are equal in measure.

INVESTIGATE

1. The opposite angles of a cyclic quadrilateral are supplementary (Cyclic Quadrilateral Conjecture).

2. The two arcs intercepted by opposite angles in the quadrilateral make up the entire circle. So, the sum of their measurements is 360°. Therefore, the sum of the angles that intercept them is $\left(\frac{1}{2}\right)360° = 180°$.

INVESTIGATION 3

SKETCH

Steps 6 and 7: Again, when constructing arcs defined by two points, selection order is important. If students get the wrong arc, they should undo their selection and try again, being careful about selection order.

INVESTIGATE

1. Parallel lines intercept congruent arcs on a circle (Parallel Lines Intercepted Arcs Conjecture).

EXPLORE MORE

To construct two tangents to circle AB from point C outside the circle, construct $\overline{CA}$ and its midpoint D. Construct circle DA and points E and F where circle DA intersects circle AB. Points E and F are points of tangency for lines drawn from point C. This works because angles AEC and AFC are inscribed in semicircles and are thus right angles.

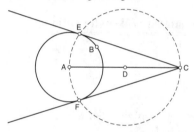

Lesson 6.4 • Tangent-Chord Conjecture DEMO

REQUIRED SKETCH

Tangent Chord Demo.gsp

LESSON GUIDE

Use this demonstration to replace or supplement the Mini-Investigation in Exercise 8 of Lesson 6.4.

INVESTIGATE

1. The measure of the angle formed by the intersection of a tangent and chord at the point of tangency is half the measure of the intercepted arc.

2. Isosceles. Two sides of the triangle are radii of the same circle, hence they are congruent.

3. By the Triangle Sum Conjecture and the Isosceles Triangle Conjecture, $m\angle AOB + 2m\angle OBA = 180°$. Therefore, $m\angle OBA = \frac{1}{2}(180° - m\angle AOB)$, or $90° - \frac{1}{2}m\angle AOB$. By the definition of arc measure, $m\overarc{AB} = m\angle AOB$, so $m\angle OBA = 90° - \frac{1}{2}m\overarc{AB}$.

4. By the Tangent Conjecture, $m\angle OBC = 90°$, so $m\angle ABC + m\angle OBA = 90°$.

5. Substitute the expression for $m\angle OBA$ from Question 3 into the equation from Question 4, and solve for $m\angle ABC$. $m\angle ABC + \left(90° - \frac{1}{2}m\widehat{AB}\right) =$ $90°$, hence $m\angle ABC - \frac{1}{2}m\widehat{AB} = 0$ and $m\angle ABC = \frac{1}{2}m\widehat{AB}$.

LESSON 6.5 · Circumference and Diameter   DEMO

REQUIRED SKETCH

Circumference Diameter Demo.gsp

LESSON GUIDE

In this demonstration, the circumference/diameter ratio (π) is represented graphically.

INVESTIGATE

1. Diameter of the circle

2. Circumference of the circle

3. 3.142

4. 3.14; the constant circumference/diameter ratio (π)

5. $y = 3.14x$ **6.** $C = \pi d$

LESSON 6.5 · The Circumference/Diameter Ratio

EXAMPLE SKETCH

Circumference.gsp

LESSON GUIDE

Use this activity in place of or as an extension to Lesson 6.5 in the student book.

SKETCH

Step 6: Selection order is important because when students trace the moving point, they'll want the diameter values on the x-axis.

INVESTIGATE

1. The point stays on a line, which means the circumference and diameter are directly proportional, or linear.

2. The slope should be about π.

3. If C is the circumference of the circle and d is the diameter of that circle, then there is a number π such that $C = \pi d$. If $d = 2r$, where r is the radius, then $C = 2\pi r$ (Circumference Conjecture).

Lesson 6.5 · Intersecting Chords Conjecture   DEMO

REQUIRED SKETCH

Intersecting Chords Demo.gsp

LESSON GUIDE

Use this demonstration to replace or supplement the Mini-Investigation in Exercise 16 of Lesson 6.5.

INVESTIGATE

1. Possible answer: $m\angle AEN$ is always between $\widehat{AN}$ and $\widehat{LG}$.

2. Average. The measure of an angle formed by two intersecting chords is the average, or one-half the sum, of the measures of the intercepted arcs.

3. $n = \frac{1}{2}m\widehat{LG}$; $s = \frac{1}{2}m\widehat{AN}$

4. $m\angle AEN = n + s$

5. $\angle AEN = \frac{1}{2}m\widehat{LG} + \frac{1}{2}m\widehat{AN}$, or $\angle AEN = \frac{1}{2}(m\widehat{LG} + m\widehat{AN})$

Lesson 6.6 · Intersecting Secants Conjecture   DEMO

REQUIRED SKETCH

Intersecting Secants Demo.gsp.

LESSON GUIDE

Use this demonstration to replace or supplement the Mini-Investigation in Exercise 9 in Lesson 6.6.

INVESTIGATE

2. The measure of the angle formed by two secants that intersect outside a circle is one-half the difference of the measures of the intercepted arcs.

3. $a = \frac{1}{2}m\widehat{AE}$; $b = \frac{1}{2}m\widehat{STN}$

4. By the Exterior Angle Sum, $b = a + m\angle C$, hence $m\angle C = b - a$. Substitute the values in Question 3 to get $m\angle C = \frac{1}{2}m\widehat{STN} - \frac{1}{2}m\widehat{AE}$, or $m\angle C = \frac{1}{2}\left(m\widehat{STN} - m\widehat{AE}\right)$.

Lesson 6.7 · Tangent-Secant Conjecture   DEMO

REQUIRED SKETCH

Tangent Secant Demo.gsp

LESSON GUIDE

Use this demonstration to replace or supplement the Mini-Investigation in Exercise 15 in Lesson 6.7.

INVESTIGATE

2. The measure of the angle formed by an intersecting tangent and secant to a circle is one-half the difference of the measures of the intercepted arcs.

3. By the Inscribed Angle Conjecture, $a = \frac{1}{2}m\widehat{CEB}$. By the Tangent-Chord Conjecture, $b = \frac{1}{2}m\widehat{BDA}$.

4. By the Exterior Angle Sum, $b = a + m\angle P$, hence $m\angle P = b - a$. Substitute the values in Question 3 to get $m\angle P = \frac{1}{2}m\widehat{BDA} - \frac{1}{2}m\widehat{CEB}$, or $m\angle P = \frac{1}{2}\left(m\widehat{BDA} - m\widehat{CEB}\right)$.

CHAPTER 7

LESSON 7.1 · Transformations and Symmetry

EXAMPLE SKETCH

Transformations.gsp

LESSON GUIDE

Use this activity in place of or as an extension to Lesson 7.1 in the student book. The activity does not cover the Reflection Line Conjecture or rotational symmetry.

SKETCH

Step 1: It's worth following the shortcut for constructing the letter.

Step 2: If it is necessary to change the labels to K and L, double-click the labels with the **Text** tool.

Step 4: To change color, use the Display menu.

Step 5: It might help to label the original letter **F** *original*. It is also fun to drag the vertices of the original **F** and observe how this affects the image shape.

Step 6: Make sure the segments are attached correctly at point N. Also, it might help students to relabel point N as *Center*.

Step 11: You might have students drag N, the center of rotation, as well.

INVESTIGATE

1. The only images that can lie directly on top of each other are the rotated and translated images, if KL = 0 and m∠MNO = 0. In this case, both images lie on top of the original.

2. **a.** It has a different location (unless the translation vector has length zero).

   b. It is congruent and has the same orientation.

3. **a.** It has a different location and is also turned at a different angle. (Again, neither statement is true if the angle of rotation is zero.)

   b. It is congruent to the original and is *not* a mirror image.

4. **a.** It has a reverse orientation from the original. It looks like a mirror image.

   b. It is congruent to the original.

LESSON 7.2 · Properties of Isometries

EXAMPLE SKETCH

Isometries.gsp

LESSON GUIDE

This activity replaces Lesson 7.2 in the student book.

INVESTIGATION 1

SKETCH

Step 1: Using the Shift key insures that all points are selected and ready to construct the polygon interior. Depending on how many points the student has made, the command in the Construct menu might be **Triangle Interior, Quadrilateral Interior, Hexagon Interior,** or **Polygon Interior**.

Step 2: Make sure students scale their axes, especially if the units of the grid are in inches. Also make sure they choose **Snap Points** from the Graph menu, although this should be the default setting.

INVESTIGATE

1. Students usually enjoy seeing the letter move and will probably want to experiment with other movements.

2. Reflection (across the y-axis)

INVESTIGATION 2

SKETCH

Step 5: Make sure students click on the actual measurements to insert them in the calculator and don't just type in values.

Step 7: To reflect point D, select it and choose **Reflect** from the Transform menu.

INVESTIGATE

1. E is the point at which the incoming and outgoing angle measurements are equal. It might be hard to get the angles exactly equal, especially if the measurements are very precise. To change precision, use the Preferences submenu in the Edit menu.

2. Drag point E so it lies on $\overline{CD'}$. This gives the minimal path for the cue ball, which is also the path of a reflection.

3. CE + ED is at a minimum when point E is at the point at which the incoming and outgoing angles are congruent. The path is minimal because it has the same length as $\overline{CD}$. CD is the shortest distance from C to D, and therefore a corresponding reflected path of the same length is the shortest path from C to the segment to D.

4. If points A and B are on one side of line ℓ, then the minimal path from point A to line ℓ to point B is found by reflecting point B across line ℓ, drawing $\overline{AB'}$, then drawing $\overline{AC}$ and $\overline{CB}$, where point C is the point of intersection of $\overline{AB'}$ and line ℓ (Minimal Path Conjecture).

REQUIRED SKETCH

Reflection Demo.gsp

LESSON GUIDE

These demonstrations cover the investigations of Lesson 7.3. You may need to explain that the motion of a reflection can be thought of as a "flip" out of the plane, as well as a movement of points across the line. These demonstrations were constructed so that the polygon appears to come out of the plane as it's being reflected.

INVESTIGATE

1. Translation

2. The direction is perpendicular to the two lines, and the distance is twice the distance between the lines.

3. Rotation

4. The angle of rotation has twice the measure of the angle between the lines.

LESSON 7.3 • Compositions of Transformations

EXAMPLE SKETCH

Reflections.gsp

LESSON GUIDE

This activity replaces Lesson 7.3 in the student book. Glide reflections are treated as a separate investigation.

INVESTIGATION 1

SKETCH

Step 2: Select the point and the line, then choose **Parallel Line** from the Construct menu.

Step 3: By a longer process, students can construct the vertex points, then select them all before choosing **Interior** from the Construct menu.

Step 4: Vertices are reflected to help measure distances in Step 6.

Step 5: The first image is already selected.

INVESTIGATE

1. The distance between the original figure and its image is twice the distance between the parallel lines.

2. Translate the original polygon by twice the distance between the parallel lines.

3. A reflection across a line followed by a reflection of the image across a second line parallel to the first is equivalent to a single translation. The distance from any point to its second image under the two

reflections is twice the distance between the parallel lines (Reflections Across Parallel Lines Conjecture).

INVESTIGATION 2

SKETCH

Steps 1–4: The point's label helps distinguish between the original figure, the first reflected image, and the second reflected image.

INVESTIGATE

1. Yes; rotation

2. When the transformed images coincide, the smaller angle between the mirror lines is exactly half the angle of rotation of the rotated image.

3. A reflection across a line followed by a reflection of the image across a second line that intersects the first line is equivalent to a single rotation. The measure of the angle of rotation equals twice the measure of the angle between the pair of intersecting reflection lines (Reflections Across Intersecting Lines Conjecture).

INVESTIGATION 3

SKETCH

Steps 1–2: It actually does not matter whether you translate or reflect first. (You might ask students to investigate this.) It's also not necessary for the vector to be parallel to the mirror line, although if it's not, the mirror line will not be the line of glide reflection symmetry.

INVESTIGATE

1. A translation is like a glide, and you also use a reflection. Therefore, this transformation is called a glide reflection.

2. Each successive footstep has the opposite orientation because it is the imprint of the opposite foot. This causes the reflection. The person's walking on the beach causes the translation, or glide.

EXPLORE MORE

1. After hiding the center of rotation, students should redo the construction from Investigation 2. After dragging the lines and changing the angles until the rotated and double reflected images coincide, they should choose **Show All Hidden** from the Display menu. They will notice that the center of rotation coincides with the intersection point of the mirror lines.

2. To create a movement button, select pairs of points, the second being the one to which the first is to move. Then choose **Movement** from the Action Buttons submenu of the Edit menu.

3. Glide reflection

LESSON 7.6 · Tessellations Using Only Translations

EXAMPLE SKETCH

Translation Tessellation.gsp

LESSON GUIDE

This activity explains how to make a tessellation using translations, starting with a parallelogram. In Explore More 2, students make a translational tessellation starting with a regular hexagon. The directions in Lesson 7.6 in the student book start with a square, so this activity is slightly more challenging and certainly covers the same material.

It's fun for students to print these sketches, but printing depends on the availability of a printer. If you don't have a color printer, remind students that color will not show up. Also, the darker shades use a lot of toner. It's a good idea to have students choose **Print Preview** from the File menu and scale their drawing to fit on a single page before they print. This will save paper.

SKETCH

This sketch contains lots of steps. If students work carefully, they shouldn't have much trouble, and they will find the end result worthwhile. When students mark vectors, they should watch the screen carefully to see it indicate the vector as marked. This helps make it clear to them what they did during that step.

EXPLORE MORE

1. This is an easy extension, and it can have dramatic results. It might be more convenient to make an Animation action button so you can turn the animation on and off. To do this, select the same point, but go to the Edit menu, choose the Action Buttons submenu, then choose **Animation.**

2. If students have trouble with this construction, they can follow the steps outlined on page 400 in their book.

LESSON 7.7 · Tessellations That Use Rotations

EXAMPLE SKETCH

Rotation Tessellation.gsp

LESSON GUIDE

This activity explains how to make a tessellation using rotations, starting with an equilateral triangle. In Explore More 1, students follow the directions from their book to make a rotational tessellation starting with a regular hexagon, and in Explore More 2 they do the same with a parallelogram. The directions in Lesson 7.7 in the student book start with a regular hexagon, then show an equilateral triangle, so the activity here covers pretty much the same material as the student book.

It's fun for students to print these sketches, but printing depends on the availability of a printer. If you don't have a color printer, remind students that color will not show up. Also, the darker shades use a lot of toner. It's a good idea to have students choose **Print Preview** from the File menu and scale their drawing to fit on a single page before they print. This will save paper.

SKETCH

Step 9: Students should include the labeled vertices in the rotation so that they will have rotation centers for future steps.

Step 10: This is a difficult process that requires careful visualizing and patience. Remind students that positive angles indicate a counterclockwise rotation. Since students used point A as a center of 60° rotations in the construction of the tile, it works as a center of 60° rotations here. Likewise, they should use point F as a center of a 180° rotation.

EXPLORE MORE

1. **and 2.** These tessellations are actually slightly simpler than the one described in the investigation. Encourage students to try them, but provide enough time to complete them.

LESSONS 7.6–7.8 · Tessellations   DEMO

REQUIRED SKETCH

Tessellation Demo.gsp

LESSON GUIDE

Don't be discouraged (and don't let students get discouraged) if students can't figure out what transformations were applied in these tessellations. They'll still enjoy playing with the demonstrations, and if you decide at some point to answer Questions 2 and 4, students will have an easier time seeing the transformations at work.

INVESTIGATE

1. Equilateral triangle

2. The left and bottom sides of the dark-shaded tile are related by a 60° rotation. The right side has point symmetry. Other tiles in the tessellation are related by 60°, 120°, and 180° rotations.

3. Parallelogram

4. The top and bottom edges of the dark-shaded tile are related by a glide reflection. The left and right edges are related by a translation. Other tiles in the tessellation are related by translations and glide reflections.

CHAPTER 8

LESSON 8.1 • Areas of Rectangles and Parallelograms

EXAMPLE SKETCH

Triangle Quad Area.gsp, page Parallelogram Area

LESSON GUIDE

Use this activity in place of or as an extension to Lesson 8.1 in the student book. In this activity students construct a rectangle and write a formula for its area in terms of its base b and height h. Then students construct a parallelogram that has the same base and height as the rectangle. By changing the shape of the parallelogram without changing its base or its height, students will observe that its area is the same as the area of the rectangle.

SKETCH

Step 1: Holding down the Shift key while constructing a segment makes it easy to construct a horizontal (or vertical) segment.

Step 2: To get both lines at once, select both points and the segment. Then choose **Construct | Perpendicular Line.**

Step 7: To show a segment's label, click once on the segment with the **Text** tool. To change the label, double-click on the label with the **Text** tool.

Step 14: Select the vertices in order, then choose **Construct | Polygon Interior.**

INVESTIGATE

1. The area of a rectangle is the product of its base and height; that is, $A = bh$, where A is the area, b is the length of the base, and h is the height of the rectangle (Rectangle Area Conjecture).

2. Side lengths AG and BH

3. Lengths b and h

4. Yes; when point G coincides with point C

5. No

6. The area of a parallelogram is the product of its base and height; that is, $A = bh$, where A is the area, b is the length of the base, and h is the height of the parallelogram (Parallelogram Area Conjecture).

EXPLORE MORE

1. If you construct an altitude from the vertex of the parallelogram to the opposite side, you can cut along this altitude to cut off a triangle. That triangle will then fit the other side of the parallelogram to form a rectangle with the same base and height.

2. You can construct the right triangle by constructing a perpendicular at one endpoint of a segment, constructing a point on the perpendicular, and connecting the vertices with segments. To make the parallelogram, extend a segment to a line through two existing points using the **Line** tool. The vertices of the parallelogram can be constructed as before.

LESSON 8.2 • Areas of Triangles and Trapezoids   DEMO

REQUIRED SKETCH

Triangle Trap Area Demo.gsp

LESSON GUIDE

These demonstrations cover Investigations 1 and 2 of Lesson 8.2. They do not cover kite area.

INVESTIGATE

1. Drag the top vertex along the line. This point is on a line parallel to the triangle's base, so dragging it doesn't change the height or base of the triangle.

2. Change the height (drag the parallel line up and down) or the length of the base (drag one of its endpoints).

3. Parallelogram; $A = bh$ 4. $A = \frac{1}{2}bh$

5. Drag segment b_1 along the line. The segment is on a line parallel to the trapezoid's base, so dragging it doesn't change the height or either base of the trapezoid.

6. Change the height (drag the parallel line up and down) or the length of either base (drag an endpoint of either base).

7. Parallelogram; $A = (b_1 + b_2)h$
8. $A = \frac{1}{2}(b_1 + b_2)h$

LESSON 8.2 • Areas of Triangles, Trapezoids, and Kites

EXAMPLE SKETCH

Triangle Quad Area.gsp, pages Triangle Area, Trapezoid Area, and Kite Area

LESSON GUIDE

Use this activity in place of or as an extension to Lesson 8.2 in the student book. In Investigations 1 and 2, students discover that any triangle or trapezoid can be doubled to form a parallelogram. By halving the area of the parallelogram, they arrive at formulas for the areas of a triangle and a trapezoid. Students derive the formula for the area of a kite by using the fact that the diagonals are perpendicular and one bisects the other.

The only purpose of the grid in this activity is to give students clearer visual feedback for their conjectures about areas.

INVESTIGATION 1

SKETCH

Step 6: Students could simply select the entire triangle and rotate it, but then they would get double points at point D and point E, which could cause confusion if labels are showing.

INVESTIGATE

1. Parallelogram   **2.** $A = bh$

3. The area of the triangle is half the area of the parallelogram.

4. The area of a triangle is half the base times the height; that is, $A = \frac{1}{2}bh$, where A is the area, b is the length of the base, and h is the height of the triangle (Triangle Area Conjecture).

INVESTIGATION 2

SKETCH

Step 7: Click once on a segment with the **Text** tool to show its label. Double-click on the label to change it. To get subscripts, type b[1] and b[2].

INVESTIGATE

1. Parallelogram   **2.** Base $b_1 + b_2$, height h

3. The area of a trapezoid is its height times the average (mean) of its bases, or half the product of its height and the sum of its bases; that is, $A = \frac{1}{2}(b_1 + b_2)h$, where A is the area, b_1 and b_2 are the lengths of the two bases, and h is the height of the trapezoid (Trapezoid Area Conjecture).

INVESTIGATION 3

SKETCH

This construction gives a kite that can be manipulated into a dart (a concave kite). The formula that students derive for area still applies.

INVESTIGATE

1. Answers will vary. The area of a kite is half the product of its diagonals; that is, $A = \frac{1}{2}d_1d_2$, where A is the area, and d_1 and d_2 are the lengths of the two diagonals (Kite Area Conjecture).

EXPLORE MORE

1. In Lesson 8.1 of this book, students construct a parallelogram whose perimeter can be changed without changing the area. They can do similar constructions for triangles and trapezoids.

2. Possible answer: The area of quadrilateral $ABCD$ is given by the formula $A = \frac{1}{2}dh_1 + \frac{1}{2}dh_2$, where d is the length of diagonal AC and h_1 and h_2 are the

lengths of the altitudes drawn to that diagonal from points B and D.

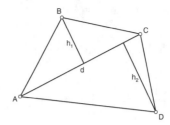

LESSON 8.4 · Areas of Regular Polygons

REQUIRED SKETCH

Polygons.gsp

EXAMPLE SKETCH

Polygon Area.gsp

LESSON GUIDE

Use this activity in place of or as an extension to Lesson 8.4 in the student book. Students will use **Custom** tools to construct regular polygons.

SKETCH

Step 1: Students can find these **Custom** tools in the sketch **Polygons.gsp,** in the **Custom Tools** folder on the CD.

Step 3: The polygon interiors just get in the way. To delete an interior, click anywhere in it to select it; then press Delete.

Step 4: To construct the center of an even-sided polygon, construct two diagonals and their point of intersection. For an odd-sided polygon, construct midpoints of two sides and connect them with segments to opposite vertices. The center is at the intersection of these segments.

INVESTIGATE

1. One triangle for each side

2. Yes; explanations will vary. Students can show the triangles are congruent using SSS, SAS, ASA, or SAA.

3. $A = \frac{1}{2}bh$

4. $A = \frac{1}{2}sa$

5. $A = (5)\frac{1}{2}sa$

6. n triangles

7. The area of a regular polygon is half its perimeter times its apothem; that is, $A = \frac{1}{2}asn$, where A is the area, a is the apothem, s is the length of each side, and n is the number of sides of the regular polygon (Regular Polygon Area Conjecture).

8. Because the length of each side times the number of sides is the perimeter, $sn = P$. Therefore, the area formula can also be written as $A = \frac{1}{2}aP$.

EXPLORE MORE

Sketches will vary.

LESSON 8.5 · Areas of Circles

REQUIRED SKETCH

To a Circle.gsp

LESSON GUIDE

Use this lesson in place of or as an extension to Lesson 8.5 in the student book. This activity uses a different approach: Instead of cutting up sectors and arranging them into a shape that resembles a parallelogram, students derive the formula for the area of a circle from the regular polygon area formula. You might choose to have students do the investigation in the book; then you can demonstrate this activity using a computer with an overhead display device.

INVESTIGATE

1. The polygon begins to fill the circle. Its area approaches that of the circle as the number of sides increases.

2. $C = 2\pi r$ **3.** $A = \frac{1}{2}aP$ **4.** $A = \frac{1}{2}rC$

5. $A = \frac{1}{2}rC = \frac{1}{2}r(2\pi r) = \pi r^2$ (Circle Area Conjecture)

EXPLORE MORE

The area of the circle is πr^2. The square has side length r, so it has area r^2. The ratio of the area of the circle to the area of the square is $\pi r^2 : r^2$, or $\pi : 1$.

CHAPTER 9

LESSON 9.1 · Three Squares   DEMO

REQUIRED SKETCH

Three Squares Demo.gsp

LESSON GUIDE

This demonstration covers Investigation 1 of Lesson 9.1.

INVESTIGATE

1. a^2 **2.** b^2 **3.** c^2

4. The sum of the areas of the squares on the legs of the right triangle equals the area of the square on the hypotenuse.

5. $a^2 + b^2$ **6.** $c^2 = a^2 + b^2$

LESSON 9.1 · The Theorem of Pythagoras

REQUIRED SKETCH

Polygons.gsp

EXAMPLE SKETCH

Pythagorean Theorem.gsp

LESSON GUIDE

This activity replaces Lesson 9.1 in the student book. The focus is not so much on the Pythagorean Theorem itself as on a proof. Be sure to save time at the end of class to go over a couple of examples of how to use the theorem, or at least direct students' attention to the examples in the book so they can do the homework.

SKETCH

Step 3: Make sure students use point B for the radius endpoint and that they don't just draw a circle that appears to pass through point B.

Step 7: Students can find a tool for drawing squares in the sketch **Polygons.gsp.** If students have trouble with squares that go the wrong way, have them undo and try again with a different selection order.

Step 9: To delete the interior, click on it to select it, then press Delete.

INVESTIGATE

1. The sum of the areas of the squares on the legs equals the area of the square on the hypotenuse (The Pythagorean Theorem).

2. Once the pieces are cut, they are no longer related to the squares from which they came. So if you change the triangle, the pieces won't fit anymore. If you want to try the experiment for a different triangle, repeatedly undo until the pieces are back in their original places, then change the triangle and repeat the experiment.

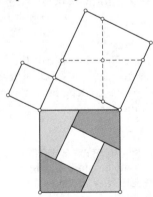

3. Because the pieces from the squares on the legs of the right triangle fit perfectly into the square on the hypotenuse, they must occupy the same area.

Therefore, the sum of the areas of the squares on the legs of the right triangle equals the area of the square on the hypotenuse.

LESSON 9.2 • The Converse of the Pythagorean Theorem

REQUIRED SKETCHES

Triple Checker.gsp, Polygons.gsp

EXAMPLE SKETCH

Pythagorean Converse.gsp

LESSON GUIDE

This activity replaces Lesson 9.2 in the student book. The approach in the book is different: Students try Pythagorean triples to see whether they work in the formula. In this activity, students start with an arbitrary triangle with squares on the sides and see that when the sum of the areas of the squares on the legs equals the area of the square on the hypotenuse, the triangle is a right triangle. Pythagorean triples are introduced as a follow-up to the main investigation.

In Question 2, students use a pre-made sketch to investigate triples.

SKETCH

Step 2: Students can find a tool for drawing squares in the sketch **Polygons.gsp.** If students have trouble with squares that go the wrong way, have them undo and try again with a different selection order.

Step 3: Click on all three interiors one at a time to select them. Choose **Measure | Area.**

Step 4: Click on a measurement in the sketch to enter it into the calculator.

INVESTIGATE

1. Students should get a right triangle. If angle measurements are off a bit, point out that students may not have been able to make the area sum exactly equal to the area of the third square. If the lengths of the three sides of a triangle satisfy the Pythagorean equation, then the triangle is a right triangle (Converse of the Pythagorean Theorem).

2. Any multiple of 3-4-5, such as 9-12-15, is a Pythagorean triple. Other triples include 5-12-13, 8-15-17, 7-24-25, and multiples of these.

LESSON 9.3 • Two Special Right Triangles

REQUIRED SKETCH

Polygons.gsp

EXAMPLE SKETCH

Special Right Triangles.gsp

LESSON GUIDE

Use this activity in place of or as an extension to Lesson 9.4 in the student book. Here students arrive at the conjectures by investigating relationships among the actual squares instead of by discovering patterns in the calculations, as in the book. Students will probably need some guidance on the last question of each investigation. You might want to go over these questions with the whole class.

INVESTIGATION 1

SKETCH

Step 1: Students can find a tool for drawing squares in the sketch **Polygons.gsp.**

INVESTIGATE

1. Because the acute angles in the isosceles right triangle are congruent and have measurements that sum to 90°, each must measure 45°.

2. $2x^2$

3. In a 45°-45°-90° triangle, if the legs have length x, then the hypotenuse has length $x\sqrt{2}$ (Isosceles Right Triangle Conjecture).

INVESTIGATION 2

SKETCH

Step 1: A **Custom** tool for an equilateral triangle can be found in the sketch **Polygons.gsp.**

INVESTIGATE

1. Because $\triangle ABC$ is equilateral, each of its angles measures 60°. Median $\overline{CD}$ divides $\triangle ABC$ into two congruent triangles, so in $\triangle BCD$, $m\angle B = 60°$, $m\angle BCD = 30°$, and $m\angle CDB = 90°$.

2. Because point D is a midpoint, $BC = 2BD$. If the side opposite the 30° angle has length x, then the hypotenuse has length $2x$.

3. $(2x)^2 = 4x^2$

4. $4x^2 - x^2 = 3x^2$

5. In a 30°-60°-90° triangle, if the shorter leg has length x, then the longer leg has length $x\sqrt{3}$ and the hypotenuse has length $2x$ (30°-60°-90° Triangle Conjecture).

Exploration • A Right Triangle Fractal   DEMO

REQUIRED SKETCH

Right Triangle Fractal Demo.gsp

LESSON GUIDE

This demonstration explores the construction in the exploration after Lesson 9.3. The required sketch has the fractal already built. The questions asked in this demo are less extensive than those in the student book or in the activity in this book. For this reason, you may wish to use the demonstration sketch along with questions from the exploration or the activity.

SKETCH

Step 2: △*ABC* is a right triangle by the Angles Inscribed in a Semicircle Conjecture.

INVESTIGATE

1. The area of the largest square (on the hypotenuse) equals the sum of the areas of the two smaller squares. That is, $(AC)^2 + (BC)^2 = (AB)^2$.

2. A triangle is built on each "branch." That triangle is constructed on the opposite side, and congruent to, the one with its hypotenuse attached to the square. Then a square is built on the side of each new triangle.

3. $(AB)^2$, or the area of the largest square, is added at each stage. First consider going from Stage 0 to Stage 1. By the Pythagorean Theorem, the sum of the areas of the two squares on the left equals the area of the square with side $\overline{AC}$, and the sum of the areas of the two squares on the right equals the area of the square with side $\overline{BC}$. Therefore, the area you add is $(AC)^2 + (BC)^2$, or $(AB)^2$. Now, going from Stage 1 to Stage 2, the sum of the areas of the two squares built on each square from Stage 1 equals the area of the square it was built on. Therefore, the area added at Stage 2 is equal to the area added at Stage 1. Continue this reasoning to inductively determine that the same amount of area is added at each stage.

4. Answers will vary. Students should choose some part of the tree that looks like a smaller copy of the original. Because some parts of the fractal overlap, this may be easier to see if they first drag point *C* so that △*ABC* is an isosceles right triangle. Sample answer:

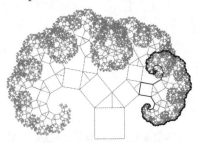

Exploration • A Pythagorean Fractal

REQUIRED SKETCH

Polygons.gsp

EXAMPLE SKETCH

Pythagorean Fractal.gsp

LESSON GUIDE

Use this activity to replace the Chapter 9 Exploration.

SKETCH

Step 1: Hold down the shift key while constructing the segment, to easily construct it horizontally.

Step 2: Select $\overline{AB}$ and choose **Construct | Midpoint.** Select first *M*, and then *B*, and choose **Construct | Circle By Center + Point.**

Step 3: Arcs are constructed counterclockwise from the first point to the second point selected.

INVESTIGATE

1. △*ABC* is a right triangle by the Angles Inscribed in a Semicircle Conjecture.

SKETCH

Step 5: Use a **Custom** tool such as 4/Square (By Edge), included in **Polygons.gsp**.

Step 6: Select *C* and $\overline{AB}$ and choose **Construct | Perpendicular Line.** Then construct a segment from *C* to the intersection of the perpendicular line with $\overline{AB}$. Hide the line and the intersection point.

INVESTIGATE

2. The area of the largest square (on the hypotenuse) equals the sum of the areas of the two smaller squares.

3. $(AB)^2$, or the area of the largest square. By the Pythagorean Theorem, the sum of the areas of the two squares on the left equals the area of the square with side $\overline{AC}$, and the sum of the areas of the two squares on the right equals the area of the square with side $\overline{BC}$. Therefore, the area you add is $(AC)^2 + (BC)^2$, or $(AB)^2$.

4. $(AB)^2$, or the area of the largest square. The sum of the areas of the two squares built on each square from Stage 1 equals the area of the square it was built on. Therefore, the area added at Stage 2 is equal to the area added at Stage 1.

5. $(AB)^2$, or the area of the largest square. Use the reasoning in the solution to Exercise 4 to inductively determine that the same amount of area is added at each stage.

6. It would have infinite area.

EXPLORE MORE

1. All of the squares that are added at any given stage have parallel corresponding sides.

2. At Stage 1: three different sizes of squares; one of the largest, two of the middle size, and one of the smallest. At Stage 2: four different sizes of squares; one of the largest, three of the next size down, three of the second-to-smallest, and one of the smallest. At Stage 3: five different sizes of squares; one of the

largest, four of the next size down, six of the middle size, four of the second-to-smallest, and one of the smallest. At stage *n*, there will be *n* + 2 different sizes. You can get the number of squares of each size by looking at the *n* + 2nd row of Pascal's Triangle.

It can be difficult to see and count the different sizes on a computer monitor, especially at Stage 3. You may want to have students print out a copy at Stages 2 and 3 and color the different sizes of outside squares.

LESSON 9.5 · Distance in Coordinate Geometry

REQUIRED SKETCH

Coordinate Distance.gsp

LESSON GUIDE

This activity replaces Lesson 9.5 in the student book. It uses a pre-made sketch, and most of the investigating is done with the calculator and with paper and pencil.

INVESTIGATION 1

INVESTIGATE

1. $AC^2 + BC^2 = AB^2$ 2. $x_C - x_A$ or $x_B - x_A$

3. $y_B - y_C$ or $y_B - y_A$

4. Answers will vary, but should be equivalent to $\sqrt{(x_B - x_A)^2 + (y_B - y_A)^2}$.

5. The distance between points $A(x_A, y_A)$ and $B(x_B, y_B)$ is given by $AB = \sqrt{(x_B - x_A)^2 + (y_B - y_A)^2}$ (Distance Formula).

INVESTIGATION 2

INVESTIGATE

1. The equation for a circle with radius *r* and center (h, k) is $(x - h)^2 + (y - k)^2 = r^2$ (Equation of a Circle).

CHAPTER 11

LESSON 11.1 · Similarity

EXAMPLE SKETCH

Similarity.gsp

LESSON GUIDE

This activity replaces most of Lesson 11.1 in the student book. This activity is shorter than the lesson but covers the same concepts. Here students have a chance to write the definition of similarity themselves. The activity does not explain similarity notation or how to solve for missing parts in similar polygons. You might start with Investigation 1 in the book, to give students a chance to

experience similarity using hand measuring tools, then continue with this activity.

SKETCH

Step 3: Select only the segments, not the endpoints. Selecting the shorter segment first marks a ratio less than 1, which shrinks objects. Reversing the selection order marks a ratio greater than 1, which enlarges objects.

INVESTIGATE

1. Dragging the center changes the position and size of the image. Changing the ratio segments changes the scale factor, making the image larger or smaller. When the ratio segments are equal in length, the image coincides with the original.

2. Yes; when the marked ratio is equal to 1, the dilated image coincides with the original figure, so all three figures are congruent.

3. All the ratios are equal, if they are all measured larger : smaller or vice versa.

4. They are congruent.

5. Two polygons are similar polygons if and only if the corresponding angles are congruent and the corresponding sides are proportional.

6. If one polygon is a dilated image of another polygon, then the polygons are similar (Dilation Similarity Conjecture).

EXPLORE MORE

1. a. The corresponding point on the image

   b. The ratio of the distances from the center to a point on the dilated image and from the center to the corresponding point on the original polygon equals the dilation ratio, which equals the scale factor.

2. Possible answer: $\triangle ABC \sim \triangle DFE$, where *D*, *E*, and *F* are the midpoints of the sides of $\triangle ABC$.

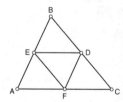

3. Possible answer: A rectangle has angles congruent to the angles in a square, but the rectangle need not be similar to the square.

4. Possible answer: A rhombus has sides proportional to the sides of a square, but the corresponding angles need not be congruent.

REQUIRED SKETCH

Similarity Shortcuts.gsp

LESSON GUIDE

This activity replaces Lesson 11.2 in the student book. The structure of the activity is slightly different. The book addresses first the AA Similarity Conjecture in Investigation 1, then the SSS Similarity Conjecture in Investigation 2, then the SAS Similarity Conjecture as well as the lack of an SSA Similarity Conjecture in Investigation 3. This activity addresses all four possible conjectures in one investigation. The different sketches in the document can be found using the tabs at the bottom. As indicated in the activity, it makes sense to share these four possible similarity conjectures among different groups in the class. Then you can have the different groups present and share their results.

INVESTIGATE

1. **a.** Any angle in the given is congruent to a pair of corresponding angles in the "triangles."

   b. Any side in the given is congruent to the corresponding side in the first "triangle" and proportional to the corresponding side in the second "triangle."

   c. The ratio in the given equals the ratio between any corresponding sides of the triangles controlled by segments in the given.

2. Encourage students to change the givens as well as the movable parts of the triangles themselves. Some givens simply can't make triangles (for example, if the three sides don't obey the triangle inequality). When students can create triangles, they should observe that they are similar except in the SSA case.

3. This gives students a chance to measure to test for similarity. Again, all cases are similar except the SSA case. Students should measure any pairs of angles not controlled by the given, as well as the ratios of any sides not controlled by the given. The corresponding angles should be congruent, and the corresponding sides should be in the same ratio as the given ratio. If the points in the fractured triangles aren't exactly coincident, the measurements may not work out precisely.

4. Students testing the SSA case can skip this step if they found a counterexample right away. If they didn't, make sure they do before they go on to Question 5.

5. Possible conjectures or examples:
   - AA Similarity Conjecture: If two angles of one triangle are congruent to two angles of another triangle, then the triangles are similar. (You might

need to discuss with students why two angles will suffice.)
   - SSS Similarity Conjecture: If the three sides of one triangle are proportional to the three sides of another triangle, then the two triangles are similar.
   - SAS Similarity Conjecture: If two sides of one triangle are proportional to two sides of another triangle and the included angles are congruent, then the two triangles are similar.
   - SSA Similarity?: Sides AB and AC are proportional and the angles at point C are congruent, but the triangles are not similar.

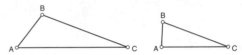

6. Students should collect all three conjectures listed in Question 5.

EXPLORE MORE

1. These are good extension projects. The constructions are not easy.

   Steps for constructing a pair of triangles constrained by AA: Construct any $\triangle ABC$ for the first triangle. Construct segment $A'B'$. To copy $\angle A$ at point A', select points B, A, and C, in that order, and choose **Transform | Mark Angle.** Double-click point A' to mark it as a center. Then select point B' and choose **Transform | Rotate.** Label the rotated point D and construct $\overrightarrow{A'D}$. Similarly, rotate A' about center B' by $\angle ABC$ to obtain point E, and construct $\overrightarrow{B'E}$. Construct the intersection of the two rays and label it C'. Hide points D and E and the two rays, and construct the necessary segments to construct $\triangle A'B'C'$.

   For the other constraints, it may be simplest to begin by constructing congruent triangles first—the command **Construct | Circle By Center+Radius** is handy here for duplicating segment lengths. Then select one entire triangle along with its vertices, and use the command **Transform | Dilate** to dilate by a marked ratio. With the dilation dialog box open, you can click either a measurement or two segments in the sketch to designate the ratio.

2. Both SAA and ASA require that two pairs of angles be congruent, so the AA Similarity Conjecture already covers these cases. The triangles must already be similar by AA, so the sides must be proportional. Adding the requirement that a pair of sides must be proportional wouldn't change anything, so both SAA and ASA are redundant similarity conjectures.

Dilation Design Demo.gsp

LESSON GUIDE

This demonstration gives the steps needed to construct the dilation design in Exploration Constructing a Dilation Design following Lesson 11.2. It's useful if you don't have time or resources for students to do the full construction themselves.

INVESTIGATE

1. For all locations of point D in the region, the figure has 8-fold rotational symmetry. If D is on the bisector of the angle forming the sector, then the figure also has 8 lines of reflectional symmetry.

2. It decreases, so the dilations produce smaller images.

3. The scale factor becomes larger than 1, so dilations occur outward rather than inward.

LESSON 11.3 · Indirect Measurement with Similar Triangles

EXAMPLE SKETCH

Indirect Measurement.gsp

LESSON GUIDE

Here students model problems similar to the investigation and example of Lesson 11.3 in the student book. Unlike that example, which demonstrates the solution, Investigation 2 here requires students to figure out the height of the tall object on their own. For this reason, this activity is a bit more challenging.

If possible, find time on another day to take students outside so they can use either of these methods to find some actual heights. (See the Exploration Indirect Measurement on page 652 in the student book.)

Either of these is a good activity in which to require students to turn in a printout, if the classroom has a printer accessible. If you plan to do this, have students answer the Investigate questions on the screen with the **Text** tool. Also have them add color and explanations to make their sketches understandable.

INVESTIGATION 1

SKETCH

Step 1: It is easy to construct a horizontal line if you hold down the Shift key while constructing it.

Step 5: To label an object, click the object with the **Text** tool. To change the label, double-click the label with the **Text** tool, then type in the new label.

Steps 7–10: The reflection of the light ray is constructed by a reflection of a geometry ray. As needed, remind

students that light rays travel along minimum paths, as in Lesson 7.2.

INVESTIGATE

1. The reflection line gets less steep as the mirror moves away from the tree.

2. Students can adjust the person or the mirror. In reality, they would probably fix the mirror and move themselves until they could see the top of the tree. The triangles are similar.

3. Students need not measure the two right angles. The measurements of the other angles should be as close as possible. It will help to measure or calculate the ratio of distances of the mirror from the person and from the tree. (These can be distances rather than lengths.)

4. Possible answer: Because the triangles are similar, write and solve a proportion statement comparing the sides.

$$\frac{\text{distance from } \textit{Tall tree} \text{ to } \textit{Mirror}}{\text{distance from } \textit{Me} \text{ to } \textit{Mirror}}$$
$$= \frac{\text{height of } \textit{Tall tree}}{\text{height of } \textit{Me}}$$

INVESTIGATION 2

SKETCH

Step 1: It is easy to construct a horizontal line if you hold down the Shift key while constructing it.

Step 5: To label an object, click on it with the **Text** tool. To change the label, double-click on the label with the **Text** tool, then type in the new label.

INVESTIGATE

1. The triangles are similar by AA. Because the angles of the sun's rays are essentially parallel, the angles the sun makes with the ground are congruent by corresponding angles (with the ground as the transversal). The angles the person and the tree make with the ground are congruent because they both measure 90°.

2. If students have trouble, they can look at the example on page 599 in their book. This example essentially gives away the process, so let students use it only as a last resort.

Possible answer: Because the triangles are similar, write proportion statements comparing the sides. Use h for the missing height of the tree.

$$\frac{\textit{Me}}{\textit{My shadow}} = \frac{\textit{Tall tree}}{\textit{Tree's shadow}}$$
$$\frac{0.52}{0.32} = \frac{h}{2.51}$$
$$h \approx 4.08$$

This means that the tree is about 408 in. tall. (Remember that 0.52 cm represented a person's height of 52 in.) So the tree is about 34 ft tall.

3. Answers should be close to the measured answers but might not be the same because of rounding. The variation will be even greater for actual measurements outdoors.

4. There are several ways to create similar triangles using the shadows of two objects at different times of day. Probably the most obvious way is to measure one shadow in the morning when the sun is in the east and the other in the afternoon when the sun makes the same angle from the west. Because the angle of inclination of the sun's rays is the same, the shadows create similar triangles. Students may think of other creative answers. Here are a few.

- If you match up the heights of the two objects and the sun's angles correctly, you can create similar triangles, with one triangle sitting on its side. For example, measure a 2-foot object when it has a 1-foot shadow, then measure a 3-foot object when it has a 6-foot shadow. These triangles are similar, with sides in proportion 1 to 3.

- Measure the objects at different times, but also in different geographic locations. For example, you might measure the first object at noon in Nashville, Tennessee, and the other, three hours later at noon in San Francisco, California. Because these cities are at approximately the same latitude, the angle of the sun should be the same. Some students will argue that these are not really different times of day.

- Measure the objects in different locations and also at different times of day at each place. Pick the locations so that the difference in latitude compensates for the difference in time of day and the sun's rays are thus at the same angle.

LESSON 11.4 · Corresponding Parts of Similar Triangles

REQUIRED SKETCH (OPTIONAL)
Similar Triangles.gsp

EXAMPLE SKETCH
Similar Parts.gsp

LESSON GUIDE
This activity replaces Lesson 11.4 in the student book. Consider splitting Questions 1–3 among different groups.

INVESTIGATION 1

SKETCH
You can save time by having students start with the prepared sketch, **Similar Triangles.gsp.** If they do, they can skip Steps 1–7.

INVESTIGATE
1. Corresponding altitudes in similar triangles are proportional to corresponding sides.

2. Corresponding medians in similar triangles are proportional to corresponding sides.

3. Corresponding angle bisectors in similar triangles are proportional to corresponding sides.

4. If two triangles are similar, then the corresponding altitudes, medians, and angle bisectors are proportional to the corresponding sides (Proportional Parts Conjecture).

INVESTIGATION 2

INVESTIGATE
1. The angle bisector in a triangle divides the opposite side into two segments whose lengths are in the same ratio as the lengths of the two sides forming the angle (Angle Bisector/Opposite Side Conjecture).

LESSON 11.5 · Area Ratios   DEMO

REQUIRED SKETCH
Area Ratio Demo.gsp

LESSON GUIDE
This demonstration shows graphically how the ratio of areas of similar figures is related to the ratio of side lengths, the concept covered in Investigation 1 of Lesson 11.5. Students should still do the investigation so that they can practice applying the concept.

INVESTIGATE
1. They have the same shape. (Corresponding angles are congruent, and corresponding sides are proportional.)

2. B

3.

Side lengths ratio	$\frac{1}{2}$	1	$\frac{3}{2}$	2	$\frac{5}{2}$	3
Area ratio	$\frac{1}{4}$	1	$\frac{9}{4}$	4	$\frac{25}{4}$	9

4. The x-axis of the plot represents the side lengths ratio, and the y-axis represents the area ratio. The plot shows that the area ratio is equal to the square of the side lengths ratio. (Its equation is $y = x^2$.)

5. Doubling the dimensions of a figure results in a figure with four times the area. So he'll need four times, not two times, as much floor tile.

LESSON 11.5 · Proportions with Area

EXAMPLE SKETCH
Area Proportion.gsp

LESSON GUIDE

Investigation 1 in Lesson 11.5 of the student book explores the relationship between the areas of similar figures. The activity here covers this concept quite thoroughly and even extends the comparison of the areas of similar figures by demonstrating the relationship on the *x*-*y* plane.

Explore More Question 2 foreshadows Lesson 11.6.

INVESTIGATION 1

SKETCH

Step 3: To construct a polygon interior, select a polygon's vertices in order, then use the Construct menu.

Step 5: *Dilate* means the same thing as *scale*. When you dilate objects, you shrink or stretch them toward or away from a center of dilation by some scale factor.

Steps 6–8: Make sure students compare parts of the dilated figure to corresponding parts of the original figure every time. If they reverse the order, the calculations will be misleading. The dilated figure's labels should be identified by the prime (′) symbol.

Step 8: You might want to have students record their predictions for the area ratios more formally, but it's fine for them just to jot them down anywhere.

Step 10: Students should get a trace of half of a parabola.

INVESTIGATE

1.

Ratio of side lengths	2	3	1	$\frac{1}{2}$	$\frac{1}{10}$	$\frac{m}{n}$
Ratio of areas	4	9	1	$\frac{1}{4}$	$\frac{1}{100}$	$\frac{m^2}{n^2}$

2. If two similar polygons (or circles) have the corresponding sides (or radii) in the ratio of $\frac{m}{n}$, then their areas are in the ratio of $\frac{m^2}{n^2}$ (Proportional Areas Conjecture).

3. The plot is half a parabola, affirming that the area ratio is the square of the side-length ratio. If the ratios were directly related, the plot would have been a straight line.

EXPLORE MORE

1. $\frac{m^2}{n^2}$ copies of a tessellating polygon will fill a dilation of that polygon by a scale factor of $\frac{m}{n}$.

2. a. If you have cubes handy, it's best to have students construct these as well as sketch them. A simple example is to compare a cube of side length 1 with a cube of side length 2. Their respective volumes are 1 and 8. So a side-length ratio of $\frac{1}{2}$ results in a volume ratio of $\frac{1}{8}$.

   b. If two similar solids have corresponding dimensions in the ratio of $\frac{m}{n}$, then their volumes are

in the ratio of $\frac{m^3}{n^3}$ (Proportional Volumes Conjecture).

The relevance of this concept can be brought home by asking students, "Why do you think the largest land animals, such as elephants and even dinosaurs, are so much smaller than the largest sea animals?" A land animal's weight must be supported by means of its skeleton. For a land animal to become twice as big, its volume—and hence its weight—would become 8 times as large. But the strength of the bones would only increase by a factor of 4, because bone strength is proportional to the cross-sectional area of the bone. As a result, the larger animal's strength-to-weight ratio would only be half what it was before, and it would have difficulty supporting its own weight. This concept is covered in more depth in the Exploration Why Elephants Have Big Ears on page 620 of the book.

LESSON 11.7 · Proportional Segments Between Parallel Lines

EXAMPLE SKETCH

Proportional Segments.gsp

LESSON GUIDE

This activity replaces Lesson 11.7 in the student book.

INVESTIGATION 1

SKETCH

Steps 6 and 7: Selection order is important when measuring ratios. Reversing selection order measures reciprocal ratios.

INVESTIGATE

1. $\triangle ABC \sim \triangle DBE$. Possible explanation: $m\angle B = m\angle B$ by identity and $m\angle A = m\angle D$ by corresponding angles, so by the AA Similarity Conjecture, $\triangle ABC \sim \triangle DBE$.

2. The ratios of corresponding segments are equal.

3. $\overline{DE} \parallel \overline{AC}$

4. Students will word this conjecture slightly differently from the wording in the student book because here they divided two sides of a triangle with a segment instead of with a line: If a segment parallel to one side of a triangle has endpoints on the other two sides, then it divides them proportionally. Conversely, if a segment cuts two sides of a triangle proportionally, then it is parallel to the third side (Parallel/Proportionality Conjecture).

INVESTIGATION 2

SKETCH

Step 3: This step constructs two lines parallel to a side of the triangle. Each line passes through the third side.

1. If two or more lines pass through two sides of a triangle parallel to the third side, then they divide the two sides proportionally (Extended Parallel/Proportionality Conjecture).

EXPLORE MORE

By extending the sides of each triangle, you can show that angles are congruent because they're corresponding angles formed by parallel lines and transversals. Therefore, the triangles are similar by the AA Similarity Conjecture.

CHAPTER 12

LESSON 12.1 • Trigonometric Ratios

EXAMPLE SKETCH

Trig Ratios.gsp

LESSON GUIDE

This activity replaces Lesson 12.1 in the student book. Students learn the definitions of *tangent*, *sine*, and *cosine*, and discover relationships and patterns among these ratios. The questions go beyond what students discover in the lesson, but if you do this activity, make sure students see examples of how to use trigonometric ratios to solve problems like the examples in the book. You should also make sure students know how to use their calculators. You might want to take two days and do this activity *and* the lesson in the book.

SKETCH

Steps 1–5: A right triangle constructed this way will be easy to scale without changing its angles. Make sure students use an equivalent method for constructing a right triangle.

Step 6: The **Text** tool turns black when the finger is positioned over an object. The letter *A* appears when the finger is positioned over a label.

INVESTIGATE

1. Yes

2. The triangle stays similar to its original shape, so side lengths stay in the same ratio.

3. $\sin A = \frac{m}{k}$; $\cos A = \frac{j}{k}$

4. $\tan 30° \approx 0.577$; $\sin 30° \approx 0.5$; $\cos 30° \approx 0.866$

5. $\tan(m\angle CAB) = \frac{m}{j}$, $\sin(m\angle CAB) = \frac{m}{j}$, and $\cos(m\angle CAB) = \frac{j}{k}$

6. As long as $m\angle A = 30°$, $m\angle C = 60°$. For acute angles A and C in right triangle ABC, $\sin C = \cos A$

because the side opposite $\angle C$ is the side adjacent to $\angle A$, and vice versa.

7. $\angle B$ is a right angle, and the triangle can have only one right angle. As $\angle A$ approaches a right angle, point C moves far away.

8. $\tan(m\angle CAB)$ gets greater and greater; $\sin(m\angle CAB)$ gets close to one; $\cos(m\angle CAB)$ gets close to zero.

9. $\sin 90° = 1$

10. $\sin 0° = 0$

11. $\tan 45° = 1$. A right triangle with a 45° angle is isosceles. Therefore, $\frac{\text{opposite}}{\text{adjacent}} = 1$.

12. $\sin 45° = \cos 45°$ because opposite = adjacent; hence $\frac{\text{opposite}}{\text{hypotenuse}} = \frac{\text{adjacent}}{\text{hypotenuse}}$.

13. $\sin x = \cos(90° - x)$

LESSON 12.3 • The Law of Sines

EXAMPLE SKETCH

Law of Sines.gsp

LESSON GUIDE

This activity replaces Lesson 12.3 in the student book. The two investigations are combined.

SKETCH

Step 3: Select *A*, *C*, and *B*, in that order, and choose **Measure | Angle**.

Step 4: Choose **sin** in the Functions submenu of the calculator, click $m\angle ACB$ in the sketch, then click OK on the calculator.

INVESTIGATE

1. Because $\sin C = \frac{h}{a}$, $h = a \sin C$.

2. The area of a triangle is given by the formula $A = \frac{1}{2}ab \sin C$, where a and b are the lengths of two sides, and C is the angle between them (SAS Triangle Area Conjecture).

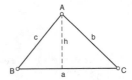

3. The three expressions all give the area of the same triangle, using a different vertex from which to measure the height. Thus, they must equal each other.

4. $\frac{\sin A}{a} = \frac{\sin B}{b} = \frac{\sin C}{c}$ (Law of Sines). Students may not think of dividing by abc. Give hints if necessary.

LESSON 12.4 • Deriving the Law of Cosines   DEMO

REQUIRED SKETCH

Law of Cosines Demo.gsp

LESSON GUIDE

This demonstration illustrates and derives the Law of Cosines from the second part of Lesson 12.4.

INVESTIGATE

1. Students may or may not see from the display that $c^2 = a^2 + b^2 - 2ab \cos C$.

2. Most students will probably not be able to verify their prediction at this point, though they should try. For a derivation, see the steps in Question 3.

3. a. Because $\cos C = \frac{d}{b}$, $d = b \cos C$.

   b. By the Pythagorean Theorem, $c^2 = (a - d)^2 + e^2$.

   c. The right side becomes $a^2 - 2ad + d^2 + e^2$. Applying the Pythagorean Theorem to the other small triangle yields $d^2 + e^2 = b^2$, so $c^2 = a^2 + b^2 - 2ad$.

   d. Replacing d with $b \cos C$ gives $c^2 = a^2 + b^2 - 2ab \cos C$.

EXPLORATION • The Unit Circle   DEMO

REQUIRED SKETCH

Unit Circle Demo.gsp

LESSON GUIDE

This demonstration replaces the Sketchpad Exploration Trigonometry and the Unit Circle. It shows how the sine and tangent ratios are related to points on the unit circle and how those ratios might be graphed as functions of the central angle.

SKETCH

Step 2: $\sin \angle BAC = \frac{CD}{AC}$, $\cos \angle BAC = \frac{AD}{AC}$, $\tan \angle BAC = \frac{CD}{AD}$

INVESTIGATE

1. AC is always 1 unit long.

2. Because $AD = x_C$, $CD = y_C$, and $AC = 1$, $\sin \angle BAC = \frac{y_C}{1}$, $= y_C$, $\cos \angle BAC = \frac{x_C}{1} = x_C$, and $\tan \angle BAC = \frac{y_C}{x_C}$.

3. 1; -1; maximum occurs at $90°$, minimum occurs at $-90°$.

4. The curve rises to a maximum height of 1 when C is at the top of the circle, then drops slowly until it reaches a minimum height of -1 when C is at the bottom of the circle.

5. $\overline{BE}$. $\triangle BAE \sim \triangle DAC$ by AA, and AB is always 1 unit, so $\tan \angle BAC = \frac{BE}{AB} = \frac{y_E}{1} = y_E$.

6. No, tangent does not have a maximum or a minimum value.

7. As $m\angle BAC$ approaches $90°$ from values less than $90°$, point E goes up farther above the x-axis. As it approaches $90°$ from values greater than $90°$, point E goes down farther below the x-axis. Thus, $\tan \angle BAC$ approaches positive or negative infinity based on which side of $90°$ you approach from.

   If you use $\triangle BAE$ for your definition of $\tan \angle BAC$, then $\tan \angle BAC = \frac{y_E}{x_E}$, where E is the intersection of $\overleftrightarrow{AC}$ with the vertical line through B. When $m\angle BAC = 90°$, $\overleftrightarrow{AC}$ is also vertical, so the intersection E does not exist. If you use $\triangle DAC$ for your definition of $\tan \angle BAC$, then $\tan \angle BAC = \frac{y_C}{x_C}$, where C is on the unit circle. When $m\angle BAC = 90°$, $x_C = 0$, so you can't divide by it. Either case shows that $\tan 90°$ is undefined. A similar argument shows that $\tan -90°$ is also undefined.

8. The curve has asymptotes at the places where C is at the top and bottom of the circle. (You may wish to review the graphing term *asymptote* here, or students may simply describe the curve as "going off" at those points.)

9. Because points C and G are traveling at the same speed, they will travel the same distance. By the time G gets to F, C has traveled exactly once around the unit circle, so has traveled a distance equal to the circumference, 2π, of the circle. Therefore, the x-coordinate of F must be $2\pi \approx 6.28$.

10. The curve will repeat itself because C will retrace its path around the unit circle.

CHAPTER 13

EXPLORATION • Hyperbolic Geometry   EXT

REQUIRED SKETCH

Poincare Disk.gsp

LESSON GUIDE

Students use The Geometer's Sketchpad to explore geometry on the Poincaré disk. Just as the surface of a sphere is a model of elliptic geometry (introduced in the Exploration Non-Euclidean Geometries), the Poincaré disk is a model of hyperbolic geometry. You might use this activity in conjunction with the Exploration so students can compare the similarities and differences between Euclidean, spherical, and hyperbolic geometry. The activity is intentionally devoid of pictures so that students will see for themselves (and be surprised by) how the tools behave.

The sketch **Poincare Disk.gsp** contains several identical pages, so students can perform a different investigation on each page. Encourage them to record observations and conjectures about each investigation in the sketch itself, using the **Text** tool.

INVESTIGATION

Step 3: Sample observations:

Hyperbolic lines are arcs of Euclidean circles that end at the edge of the disk. They meet the edge of the disk at right angles.

Hyperbolic circles are like Euclidean circles except that their centers are skewed toward the edge of the disk.

The closer a hyperbolic line or segment comes to passing through the center of the disk, the straighter it is.

Hyperbolic distances increase as you move toward the edge of the disk.

If two hyperbolic segments have a common endpoint near the edge of the disk, the measure of the angle they form is close to 0. (Students aren't likely to notice it, but hyperbolic angle measurements are defined by the tangents to the arcs where two Poincaré segments or lines meet to form an angle.)

Step 4: The hyperbolic line meets the edge of the disk at right angles.

Step 5: Infinitely many hyperbolic lines can be drawn that don't intersect the given one. Poincaré geometry is based on Assumption 1: Through a given point not on a given line there pass more than one line parallel to the given line.

Step 6: Radii that go toward the center of the disk appear longer than radii that go toward the edge. Distances near the edge of the disk get compressed.

Step 7: The sum of the angle measurements in a hyperbolic triangle is strictly between 0° and 180°.

Step 8: The base angles of an isosceles triangle are congruent. This theorem of Euclidean geometry can be proved without the use of the parallel postulate, so it's true in this non-Euclidean geometry as well.

Step 9: Encourage students to try constructions and investigations of their own.

SUGGESTED EXPLORATIONS:

1. Is it possible to circumscribe a hyperbolic triangle? (This can be done with the **Hyperbolic P. Bisector** and the **Hyperbolic Circle by CP** tools.)

2. Is it possible to inscribe a circle in a hyperbolic triangle? (This can be done with the **Hyperbolic A. Bisector,** the **Hyperbolic Perpendicular,** and the **Hyperbolic Circle by CP** tools.)

3. Can you construct a hyperbolic centroid? A hyperbolic orthocenter? (Both answers are yes.)

Key Curriculum Press

Innovators in Mathematics Education

Comment Form

Please take a moment to provide us with feedback about this book. We are eager to read any comments or suggestions you may have. Once you've filled out this form, simply fold it along the dotted lines and drop it in the mail. We'll pay the postage. Thank you!

Your Name _____

School _____

School Address _____

City/State/Zip _____

Phone _____ Email _____

Book Title _____

Please list any comments you have about this book.

_____

_____

_____

_____

_____

_____

_____

_____

_____

_____

Do you have any suggestions for improving the student or teacher material?

_____

_____

_____

_____

_____

_____

_____

To request a catalog or place an order, call us toll free at 800-995-MATH or send a fax to 800-541-2242. For more information, visit Key's website at www.keypress.com.

Fold carefully along this line.

BUSINESS REPLY MAIL
FIRST CLASS   PERMIT NO. 338   EMERYVILLE, CA

POSTAGE WILL BE PAID BY ADDRESSEE

Key Curriculum Press
Innovators in Mathematics Education

Attn: Editorial Department
1150 65th Street
Emeryville, CA 94608-9740

Fold carefully along this line.